To
Brian

Christmas 1973

From

Harry and Bill

D0445450

Canada
Eh to Zed

Canada
Eh to Zed

A
Further
Contribution
to the
Continuing
Quest
for the Elusive
Canadian
Identity

Mervyn
J.
Huston

Hurtig
Publishers
Edmonton

Hurtig Publishers
10560-105 Street
Edmonton, Alberta

ISBN
0-88830-071-9

Illustrated by
Roy Peterson

Designed, typeset,
printed and bound
in Canada

This
book
is
dedicated
to
Kevin

Contents

CHAPTER ONE

The Samarkand Fan

I was sitting in the backyard with my clipboard on my knee, trying to write a paper, when Mr. Zeppelin came along in his garbage truck. He and his helper descended from the cab and emptied our trash cans, then came to the back fence and hailed me with a friendly greeting.

"What are you doing today, Professor?" asked Mr. Zeppelin.

"I'm looking for the Canadian identity," I answered.

"The Canadian what?"

"Identity, the Canadian identity."

"Oh, that!" Mr. Zeppelin waved his hand disparagingly. "Maybe

9

it's been thrown out with the rest of the garbage. Would you like me to keep an eye out for it? We've come across some pretty interesting stuff today, including a left-handed corkscrew and a stuffed gopher. It could turn up in someone's load."

I grinned at him. "You may be right."

"Then I'll keep looking. What's it worth if I find it? Ten cents?"

"A million dollars."

"Then I'll keep a lookout as sharp as a mother with a virgin daughter at a pharmacists' convention."

"I should add that the million dollars is payable in gratitude."

"Then I won't bother. Gratitude is petty currency."

Mr. Zeppelin was appropriately named as he had a shape like a dirigible. He was a huge man who walked with a swagger, Alberta ranchman's style-that is, with his elbows out and his hands dangling loosely. His large mouth was surmounted by a formidable grey walrus mustache. He had baggy, basset hound eyes which crinkled with good humour under shaggy eyebrows. One eyebrow had a tendency to go up in a disconcertingly quizzical fashion when he was listening to you. He had a deep, resonant, bass voice which rumbled up from his cavernous interior. When he laughed, his belly bounced up and down like a watermelon on a yo-yo string. His laugh was a deep chuckle, a heavy "huff, huff, huff." He always wore immaculate grey overalls and a grey trainman's hat with a long peak. His partner, in contrast, was a skinny little fellow with a happy, vacuous face.

Mr. Zeppelin was a great talker who was not, I suspected, unduly hampered by veracity. In our frequent chats over the back fence I had always found him amiable and knowledgeable. He was surprisingly well read, and possessed a wealth of information and misinformation which he was happy to share. He had a tendency to use big words which he usually applied correctly. As I got to know him better, I developed a strong suspicion that many of his malapropisms were deliberate and sometimes designed as traps; it took me a long time to learn how to avoid these traps. He had a strange, droll sense of humour which I had difficulty coping with. Like all academics I am of a serious turn of mind with a regrettably poor ear for humorous nuances. I never knew for certain when he was pulling my leg and when he wasn't; as a result, I had been led far up the garden path more than once.

"Come in and sit awhile, if you have a few minutes," I invited. "Maybe you can help me with my treatise."

"Maybe I could at that," he allowed. "I guess the city D.D. can afford some time in the interests of esoteric scholarship."

10

"D.D.?" I asked.

"Detritus Detail," he explained grandly. He turned to his assistant and shouted, "Tend to the horses, Robespierre! Loosen their cruppers and splice their binnacles. If the mayor calls on the hot line tell him I am in conference and cannot be awakened."

"Sure thing!" replied his helper with a grin and he returned to the truck, lighting a cigarette.

Mr. Zeppelin came in through the garden gate and settled his huge bulk into a creaking lawn chair beside me. He pushed back his cap, disclosing a completely bald, high-domed pate. He removed his gloves, folding them neatly before laying them on the grass at his side. His large hands were carefully manicured. On the little finger of his left hand he wore a ring with an intricately carved green stone. Noticing my scrutiny he held it up for my inspection.

"I see you are admiring my bauble. The stone was originally a belly button ornament worn by a Balinese dancer in Macao. She got the hiccups and it popped right into my glass of pernod. I've kept it for sentimental reasons. Also it's quite valuable-a green ruby, rather rare."

"How do you account for that?"

"She had indigestion from eating a *foie gras* and horseradish sandwich."

"No, I meant-," I paused and thought better of it. "That certainly explains it," I nodded solemnly. He looked a little disappointed. He continued to study the stone.

"Thus began a beautiful friendship," he mused, "which was terminated by the Canadian immigration authorities. She had no criminal record, no history of subversion, nor connections with the Mafia so she was not admitted. Pity." He sighed deeply. "But enough of idle reminiscences."

He cocked a quizzical eyebrow at me. "So you're searching for the Canadian identity. What are you going to do with it if you find it?"

"I'm giving a paper at a learned society meeting."

"To a bunch of professors?"

"Yes."

"Then you had better keep it simple." He grinned sardonically at me.

"I wish I could resent that."

"Don't waste your time. But I thought you were a real scientist. How come a guy like you is studying a fuzzy subject like the Canadian identity? I thought that kind of malarky was handled by the sociable scientists."

"True, such a subject properly falls within the purview of social scientists, but they have tried it and failed. The trouble with specialists is that they can't see the culture for the bacteria. They know too much and overshoot the mark. So I thought there might be some advantage to a non-specialist tackling the job. A mind trained in science, uncontaminated by preconceptions and unhampered by knowledge, may see through the fuzz where others have failed. The dilettante may confound the specialist. Fools rush in and all that. At any rate, I bring to the subject a fearless ignorance."

"No argument there, Professor. And if what you need in a collaborator is fearless ignorance, you've come to the right man. When it comes to ignorance, I take second place to no one. Also, since I am a typical, dyed in the wooly-headed, middle-class Canadian, I can be your guinea hen for experimentation."

"Pig. Guinea pig," I objected. "You don't use guinea hens for experimentation."

"I thought we were tilling new ground. Anyhow, since Canadians are chicken, a guinea hen would be more apt. Furthermore-,"

"Okay, okay, I'll concede the point!" I held up my hands in surrender. "Let us agree to combine our talents as typical middle-class Canadians in search of our identity. It's time, I'm convinced, that the Canadian scene was viewed from within rather than from above by someone on a self-constructed pinnacle. At any rate, our naivete will be refreshing and appealing."

"Everybody else has had a whirl at it, so why shouldn't we? How far have you got to date?"

"Not very far, only the title." I showed him the sheet with the title on it, "The Canadian Identity."

"An excellent beginning," he allowed. He leaned back comfortably in his chair and crossed his legs. "I also have furrowed my brow on the subject of the Canadiamania for an identity. It's like trying to prove you're alive. It's not easy. Canadians think they exist because they think they exist. And vice versa." He took off his cap and rubbed his glossy head. "But the continued search by Canadians for an identity is a manifestation of a national neuritis which-,"

"Neurosis. Neuritis is an inflammation of the nerves."

"That's what I mean! The Canadian people have developed an inflammation of their nerves over this search for identity. But they won't find it. The search is the discovery." He looked at me with sad eyes.

"That is sufficiently cryptic as to sound profound. Has it been said before?"

He heaved a sigh. "Probably. Everything worth saying has been said, and a good deal not worth saying, too."

"True on the last point at least. But let us not be defeatists about this or we won't get anywhere at all."

"How do you propose going about the establishment of the Canadian identity, Professor? Indeed, what sort of animal are we looking for?"

"A good question and a good place to start, I would think." I chewed the end of my pen. "I suppose a national identity is the sum of the characteristics and attitudes of the individual members of that nation. These traits produce cultural and political institutions which will be typical of that country. Such behavioral patterns give the country a characteristic personality which is recognizable as unique and constitutes an identity. How's that?"

"Good up to a point," Mr. Zeppelin nodded. "In your thesis, however, the first step you mentioned was a sum of individual characteristics. If this is valid then the problem is simple. You compile these figures, add them up, divide by the number involved, and there you are. That's the scientist in you coming out. It won't work. It's just not that simple. You can't arrive at an individual's personality in that manner. So how much less is it possible with a nation of twenty-one million souls?"

"You can use statistics."

"Statistics, the scientists' panacea; the crutch of the incompetent; the obfuscator of tenuous theories." He struck himself on the forehead with the flat of his hand. "A fig for statistics! I have the greatest admiration for pure mathematics; my don at Oxford taught me that pure mathematics is the only true science. In the temple of Athene, mathematics is pure, incorruptible and sublime. But when she ventures out into the market place she becomes a harlot, selling her services to all. Statistics is her pimp. Oh, the shame of it." He held up his arms in mock horror.

"Ah, ahem, yes, but harlots have their utility."

"Great heavens to Betsy on a bicycle, Professor, you astound me!"

"I wasn't always a bishop," I smirked. I tried on my sophisticated man-of-the-world look. It didn't come off too well.

"I shall not sit in moral judgement on your regrettable lapse," smiled Mr. Zeppelin roguishly. "Indeed, who am I to do so, I who have favoured the ladies from Singapore to Medicine Hat?"

I looked over my shoulder to make sure my wife hadn't been within earshot. "A figure of speech only," I explained lamely.

"Of course, of course." Mr. Zeppelin favoured me with a broad wink. "But to return to the safer subject of statistics. You won't establish a Canadian identity with a computer. That's where all the others have failed. The Canadian personality is a mystique, not a mathematical symbol. You can't assess a mystique with an adding machine, any more than you can evaluate a symphony by adding up all the sharps, flats, quivers and semidemi quivers. Oh, you need me in this investigation, Professor, I can see that. Science can count the petals on the rose, but cannot appreciate its beauty. Although I am scientifically trained myself by some of the great leaders of the scientific world, I am also a humanist. This quality may be sufficient to modify and mellow your scientific crassitude."

"We shall hope so," I agreed equably. "Then let us try to maintain a balance between the frigidity of science and the warmth of humanism."

"If we are to err let us do so on the warm side. You can't cook a bannock on a cake of ice-to quote an old Armenian folk-saying I just made up."

"Agreed." I tapped on the clipboard with my pen. "One concept fraught with difficulties into which we have immediately stumbled is our reference to ourselves as 'typical' Canadians. The purists say there is no such animal and to talk about one is to confuse the issue rather than to clarify it. You and I epitomize nicely the dilemma. You weigh a hundred pounds more than I do; I am a scientist, you are a humanist; I am a professor, you are, ah-,"

"A garbageman. I deplore euphemisms."

"In view of our diversity, how can we both be typical Canadians?"

"We are typical because of our diversity."

"A paradox."

"Quite."

"The paradox of typicality would appear to be inherent in the concept of a national identity." I continued, feeling my way. "If there is a Canadian identity then there is a typical Canadian. It's true, strictly speaking, that he doesn't exist any more than any other biological average exists. There isn't any average rat or frog or, say, guinea hen, in experimental work either, but this doesn't invalidate the experiment. Normalcy does not exist as an entity since what is considered a norm is a mathematical mean of characteristics of subjects assumed to be normal."

"It is a characteristic of the average man to believe he is above average," said Mr. Zeppelin.

"I presume we are no exception," I smiled.

"Of course." Mr. Zeppelin tossed his cap in the air, catching it adroitly. "I think our purist friends have gone awry, however, in taking the term 'typical' as a cinnamon for 'stereotype'-such as the polite Englishman, the dour Scot or the inscrutable Chinese. The stereotype is a caricature foisted on a nationality by others, whereas the typical is a philosophical concept based on a synthesis of characteristics, even if he doesn't exist. I hope that came out right." Mr. Zeppelin scratched his head. "I seem to have got myself ensnarled in the convolutions of my own rhetoric."

"It sounded fine to me," I said, "and sufficiently contorted to pass for the usual erudite sociological jargon. The snare of 'average' is demonstrated in the observation that the average Canadian family includes 2.7 children. You don't find seven-tenths of a child in many homes that I know of."

"You don't get around much, Professor."

I hurried along before he could develop the theme. "I take it then that we have convinced ourselves that the concept of a typical or average Canadian is a logical corollary to the notion of a national identity. We shall accept the term 'typical Canadian' in the *modus operandi* of our deliberations recognizing the spuriousness of the conceit."

"Agreed with alacrity," nodded Mr. Zeppelin. "I couldn't have said it better myself."

"One problem with amateurs and neophytes in a new field of investigation," I continued, "is that they always start farther back in their dissertation than is necessary. I suspect that we are belabouring the obvious."

"Belabour away, my friend. I haven't enjoyed myself so much since I fell into a vat of ouzo in a Corinth brothel." He smiled happily, patting his paunch. "Proceed, Professor, with your Socratic technique."

"Okay," I grinned at him. "As an opening gambit let me pose the question, what is a Canadian?"

"A Canadian is like anybody else-only better."

"Why is he better?"

"Because he is a Canadian."

"That seems to have gone in a circle to bring us back to where we started."

"Good," said Mr. Zeppelin. "Then we haven't lost any ground."
He looked at me expectantly.

"You have proposed yourself as a quote, typical Canadian. What credentials do you present in support of your contention?"

"I have many such credentials, some of which are creditable. Number one, I'm confused as to what I am."

"Good. Certainly very typical."

"For another, I have a good start in that my father was English and my mother was French. But a Canadian is a compost of many nationalities-,"

"Composite," I corrected.

"Yes, that also. In addition to English and French I can lay claim to a variety of other typically Canadian blood lines in that of my six grandparents, one each was Greek, Ukrainian, Swedish, Italian, Hungarian and North American Indian."

"With grandparents like that how did you end up with an English father and a French mother?"

"It's genetics. It's all done with genetics," he answered expansively. "You ought to make a study of it, my boy. Very interesting. I spent some time on the subject when I was at the Sorbonne. You see-,"

"I'll let that pass, but how come you had six grandparents?"

"Simple mathematics. If you'll just calculate-,"

"Most people have just four."

"Hmm?" He counted on his fingers. "You're right of course. I forgot to mention that two of my grandparents were married twice."

"Ah, yes, to be sure. That accounts for it nicely."

"To continue." He gave me an aloof look. "With my heterosexual ethical background-,"

"Ethnic."

"That's right. Look, Professor, if I'm going to help you, you've got to listen better."

"Sorry. I apologize."

"Accepted." A graceful wave of the hand. "So with my polylinguistic background-," he paused and I nodded, "I represent much of the Canadian racial mosaic in one package. A large package to be sure." He patted his paunch with satisfaction and a deep "huff, huff, huff."

"The name Zeppelin is German, isn't it? That is one nationality you didn't mention."

"An oversight. Yes, it is. I am somewhat embarrassed to disclose that the original paternal family name was Bagogas, a distinguished Hungarian dynasty, I might add. It was changed by my great-grandfather to Zeppelin. I must confess that much of the impetus for the change of name was due to a desire to avoid the attentions of a certain Kurdish nobleman who was annoyed with my great-grandfather after a daring escape down a rope made of jasmine-scented bedsheets from a Turkish seraglio, on a camel."

16

"The camel slid down the rope?"

"Certainly not! My great-grandfather did. He escaped across the desert on a camel. Camels are very intelligent animals but have no talent at all for sliding down ropes."

Mr. Zeppelin ignored my sigh of exasperation and continued. "Well, anyhow, my esteemed ancestor felt it expedient to change his name, as I explained. His Hungarian mother was part German and bore the name of Zeppelin so he simply adopted her family name. A fortuitous juxtaposition of names, wouldn't you say?"

"I certainly would. Almost unbelievable."

"Truth is sometimes a stranger to fiction."

"And vice versa."

"Agreed." He threw back his head and laughed with a great "huff, huff, huff."

"Now, what racial notes do you bring to the Canadian symphony?" he asked.

"I'm fifty percent Irish, fifty percent Scottish, and ten percent a mixture of other lines including English, Dutch and Austrian." I held up my hand. "I realize that comes to over one hundred percent and in all modesty I admit it."

He laughed, "Well, between us I'd say we have the muskeg covered."

"We do indeed." I shuffled my papers. "We seem to have strayed from the object of the exercise we have set ourselves. Back to the Canadian identity."

"By all means." Mr. Zeppelin nodded his head graciously.

"Okay. Where do we pick it up? I suppose we should explore certain fundamentals and, ah, basics. There is a splendid axiom much quoted in academic circles, but seldom followed, which goes like this: the place to begin is at the beginning."

"Oh, splendid," applauded Mr. Zeppelin, clapping his hands. "Begin at the beginning. Marvellous. Excellent. I suppose it would take a group of professors to come up with a stunner like that. Tell me, what is an academic circle? Is that the circle academics go in during the course of their discussions?"

"No, no. The term academic circle refers to any group of professors functioning on a campus."

"Thank you, thank you." Mr. Zeppelin pursed his lips and stroked his mustache. "That helps a lot. I was afraid-but no matter. Proceed."

I looked at him suspiciously but he met my scrutiny with a bland expression. "Let us first endeavour to paint with a broad brush. We shall fill in the details later," I suggested.

17

He nodded sagely. "A sound way to begin at the beginning, in the academic manner."

"Well, what is the chief characteristic of the Canadian scene? What first hits you in the eye?"

"A snowball?" Mr. Zeppelin chuckled deeply. "Excuse me, Professor, I am being fictitious. Hmm." He tugged at his mustache. "I have no objection to saying the obvious. The obvious is often very obscure, as in this case. Let me see. I would say the principal feature of the Canadian scene is that it is characterized by a completely classless society." He nodded solemnly. "Yes, that is it. A classless society."

"What do you mean, a classless society?"

"A social structure without stratification into classes, a situation where everyone is equal. Do you agree?"

"Yes, yes, I do," I said enthusiastically. "An absence of classes is certainly a prominent feature of the Canadian scene and you are very astute to have picked it out immediately."

"You mean I've hit my thumb on the head right off the bat?"

"Yes, you have."

"Good." He looked inordinately pleased with himself. "My gracious, but it's hot today!" He removed his cap to fan himself. "Robespierre," he shouted suddenly to his assistant, "bring the Samarkand fan of Persian peacock feathers, will you?"

"What you want?" called Robespierre from the truck.

"The large shovel, you neanderthal nincompoop."

"Okay, Mr. Zed," answered Robespierre.

Robespierre came into the yard carrying a huge shovel which he brought to Mr. Zeppelin. "Here you are, Mr. Zed," he said politely.

"Thank you, my good man," said Mr. Zeppelin graciously. "I find it hot here today. Would you kindly stand behind the Professor and fan us with the shovel. This will waft gentle breezes about our fevered brows as we struggle with the philosophical concept of equality."

Robespierre took up a position behind our chairs where he waved the shovel backward and forward over our heads. It had a certain aroma about it.

"Ah, much better," sighed Mr. Zeppelin contentedly. "So, professor, I believe we had accepted the hypotenuse that the Canadian scene is characterized by a classless society."

"Yes, we had. I believe very strongly that a tradition of complete equality is one of the basic strengths of the Canadian way of life. But is this unique to Canada?"

18

"Yes, it is," said Mr. Zeppelin firmly. "No other country of the world has a society that is as lacking in class as that of Canada."

"I wonder why that is."

"It may be that Canada, being a relatively new country, has not had time to develop a class structure." He turned his head to Robespierre. "Faster, you scoundrel. You are slacking on the job. Faster."

"Sure," said Robespierre, speeding up his swing.

I was having some difficulty in concentrating with the shovel waving backward and forward a few inches above my head. The aroma had become more noticeable. I glanced up apprehensively, making a comparison of the weight of the shovel with Robespierre's skinny arms.

"Look, Mr. Zeppelin," I said diffidently, "I appreciate your kindness in providing the fan but I am a little worried I might be decapitated. I feel I am sitting under a sword of Damocles. I'd really just as soon you didn't bother."

"Very well. As you wish. Cease and desist, varlet," he shouted at Robespierre. "Remove yourself a little distance, and down wind if you will. Over on yon chair in the shade will do nicely."

"Okay, Mr. Zed," said Robespierre amiably. He slouched over to the chair where he proceeded to pick his teeth with a rusty nail.

"It is hot today," I observed. "Possibly I can relieve our distress in another way. Would you care for an ice-cold beer?"

"Ah, that would be nectar indeed."

"Would your colleague care to join us in a glass?"

"I am sure he would appreciate a foaming pint but it wouldn't be fitting for him to join us. He could have one over yonder. Do you have anyone in your house, some attendant who does menial chores, who could keep him company and pass the time in gentle persiflage?"

"The only person who answers that description would be my wife."

"Then see if she would be so gracious as to join him."

When I went into the house to get the beer I made the proposal delicately to my wife. She suggested I go climb a pine tree. When I returned to the yard with a tray of beer, I told Mr. Zeppelin that my wife was defrosting the oven or something and wasn't available.

"Pity," he said. "Robespierre gets along very well with the ladies. He isn't very bright." I looked at him sharply but he returned my scrutiny with a look of complete ingenuousness.

I presented each of my guests with a bottle and a stein.

Robespierre thanked me with a cheerful grin. Mr. Zeppelin poured his beer carefully into the stein, held it up in my direction, uttered a hearty "salud" and drained it down. He sighed luxuriously and smacked his lips. He wiped his large mustache with the back of his hand, eructating gently. "That hit the spot with a splash," he smiled appreciatively.

"Would you care for another?"

"Not at the moment, thank you. I must let my asthmatic balance readjust itself."

I seated myself and sipped at my beer. "Now let us return to our discussions, as I do feel we are making excellent progress. To recapitulate, you have suggested that Canada is a classless society, right?"

"That is my postulate," he rumbled. "Do you find it defective?"

"No, no. By no means. But let us go on from there. How does the classless society function?"

Mr. Zeppelin closed one eye and blew through his mustache. He spoke slowly. "Every Canadian feels he's as good as anyone else, and better than most. Thus he recognizes no superiors-only inferiors-which is gratifying. Man is aware of a class structure only if he sees classes above him. A class structure does not exist if it is not recognized and accepted as such. Therefore, the Canadian scene is classless." He opened his eyes wide with a look of happy accomplishment.

"But surely a person can see that others have more money, or power, or prestige, or whatever," I objected.

"Aha." Mr. Zeppelin held up his hand and counted on his fingers. "First, prestige. Prestige is not intrinsic. It is a status accorded by others and can be withdrawn at whim or by design. Secondly, power. Power arises only from two sources, money and elected office. The latter is unstable and the former theoretically obtainable. Therefore, none of these factors makes others truly superior."

"How about birth?"

"Superiority by birth does not exist in Canada, although it does in all other countries of the world, including the United States, although they pretend otherwise. The prestige of birth exists only in the minds of pretenders to that status. The silver spoon is a baby's soother for the permanently immature. I can speak thusly since I count among my ancestors many aristocrats including a Hungarian nobleman, an Indian chief and a Russian prince. But I do not trade on my rich heritage of royal blood. They were all scoundrels anyway." He smiled wryly and I felt with a degree of false modesty.

"You talk like a westerner."

"I do because I am. And proud of it. All Canadians are wonderful people, but westerners are the Canadianissimos-the crème de la crème."

"Since I am also a westerner, I am not apt to disagree."

"Of course not. There are none so compatible as bigots whose prejudices coincide." He heaved himself out of his chair. "On this happy note of concord, I shall take my leave. The vanguard in the battle against pollution must continue upon its way. Thank you for the beer, Professor."

"You're very welcome. I have enjoyed our discussion immensely. I hope you will return tomorrow so we may continue it."

"I shall be delighted. Robespierre and I will be in the neighbourhood about this time and we shall drop in on you."

"I shall have a warm welcome cooling in the refrigerator."

"Knave, varlet, scoundrel!" he roared at Robespierre, who was dozing in the shade. "Up on your feet. We must be off to collect the debris defecated by the classless society. Please bring the limousine around to the back portico, my good man." He waved his hand grandly and Robespierre ambled forward.

I walked with them out to the truck. Mr. Zeppelin assured me they would return on the morrow. They clambered into the truck and with a wave and a toot they bounced up the alley.

CHAPTER TWO

The Easter Bunny & the Tooth Fairy

The next day I waited with considerable impatience for Mr. Zeppelin's arrival. I thought over our previous day's discussion with a vague feeling of unease which I could not quite identify. I shrugged it off to devote my attention to plans for continued explorations.

The truck finally rumbled up the alley with its two passengers waving cheerfully. The truck was parked and they climbed down from the cab to join me in the backyard. Mr. Zeppelin took his chair at my side while Robespierre withdrew to his place under a tree. I immediately brought out cold beers which were welcomed with enthusiasm and disposed of with dispatch.

"This will lubricate the old brain cells," said Mr. Zeppelin, tossing off his stein of beer after a polite "salud" in my direction. He settled himself comfortably in his chair before fixing me with his eyebrow-elevated, quizzical look. "Well, Professor, where do we go today in our search for the elusive Canadian identity?"

"I've given some thought to procedures," I said eagerly. "I would propose the following *modus operandi*: we shall take up in turn various facets of Canadian life and explore them in depth-politics, education, business, women and so forth. Then when we have finished we should be able to fit the pieces of the jigsaw together to form a picture of the Canadian identity. Okay?"

"Agreed."

"We shall be considering what Canadians actually are-what they think, what they feel, how they behave-not what they ought to think or feel or be. In other words, we shall not be unduly concerned with the rights or wrongs of their position."

"Good. That will remove an awkward moral dilemma," observed Mr. Zeppelin.

"We can compare the Canadian attitude with that of other countries in order to establish that which is peculiarly Canadian. We shall particularly use the United States as a point of reference in each area. We shall try to see how Canadians differ from Americans. Everyone knows what an American is."

"They do?"

"Yes. At least they have an identity with which we can contrast our own. The particular fear of every Canadian is that we are just second-rate Americans and-,"

"An attitude shared by Americans," grumped Mr. Zeppelin.

"But are we?"

"Certainly not," said Mr. Zeppelin vehemently.

"Spoken like a true Canadian. Then tell me how we differ from them, or are as good, or better."

"There's lots of ways." He waved his hand grandly.

"Name one."

"Our table manners are better; we're politer; our garbage disposal system is better; our-,"

"Who made your truck?"

"General Motors."

"Go on."

"We treat the blacks better."

"We don't have many. And how about the way we treat our Indians?"

"Humph! We're more honest and law abiding."

"We're more apt to get caught."

"We don't fight unpopular wars."

"No wars are popular. And we don't have an army big enough to frighten Zambia. You can't take credit for not doing something you can't do."

"We're more modest."

"For modest read inferiority complex."

"Hey, whose side are you on?" he demanded.

"Nobody's. I'm just trying to find a foothold somewhere."

"Anyhow you said we didn't have to be right or justify our attitudes; all we are trying to do is establish the Canadian outlook. What I have been saying is what Canadians think, right or wrong."

"Do I gather from your comments that you think Canadians are anti-American, to use the usual cliché?"

"Certainly not. We find Americans annoying but then every country finds other countries annoying. It's an aspect of mild byjingoism. Usually you can ignore foreigners but you can't ignore somebody you're sharing a bed with if they have the hiccups."

"Particularly an elephant with the hiccups, to adapt the simile of the pundit of our time."

"In spite of the hiccups, Canadians and Americans are very good friends really. Like all good friends each is happy to give advice but not to receive it. Canada is perfectly prepared to tell the States how to run their affairs but when they reciprocate we tell them to mind their own bloody business. A normal human relationship. It should not be confused with emnity."

"Do you think that Canadians really feel the Canadian way of life is superior to the American?"

"Yes, I do. Definitely," said Mr. Zeppelin firmly.

"Then why don't Canadians toot their own horns more?"

"They are turned off by the din from below the border. Braggadocio is in bad taste in Canada. It's a way of life with the Americans. Canadians have their revenge in smug superiority. This is a subtlety lost on the Americans who are the most unsubtle people on earth. Their brashness is their charm-if you can stand it."

"Yes, Americans have a youthful exuberance and a gauche naivete which is a bit jarring on more sophisticated peoples," I agreed. "Americans support their team with fervor and irrationality. Rah, rah. Theirs is the best team despite all evidence to the contrary. If things go awry, they boo the umpire, whether it's the man-in-blue or the United Nations General Assembly. To a Canadian, it's a dull chess game which he expects to lose."

"Yeah," said Mr. Zeppelin. "An American is full of helium; a

Canadian is full of porridge."

"What other traits do you see which characterize the Americans?"

"By my observations, the States are characterized by slack-bellied men and fat-assed women."

"Oh, go on. Have you been to Las Vegas recently? After seeing the dollies in the shows there you begin to wonder if your wife belongs to the same species."

"Yes, it's been said that the Canadian housewife is like a cream puff with no whipped cream in it."

"I disagree."

"You'd better." He glanced up at our kitchen window with a broad grin. "But to get back to the States," he continued, "what really frosts a Canadian's britches is the amazing ignorance of the Americans about Canada. It's no wonder, I suppose. The only reference to Canada you'll hear on their television, which is their only educational media, is 'there's a cold front moving in from Canada.' They get the idea Canada is a gigantic refrigerator. A Texan turns up for a midsummer holiday in Canada wearing a parka. And I presume a fur-lined jockstrap-Americans have a high regard for their genitalia. He thought there'd be snow on the ground. I once asked a guy in a bar in New Orleans, by way of experimentation, what a Canadian was. He said 'an American who plays hockey for Montreal.' How about that, sport fans?" He slapped his knee in exasperation.

"Yes, I know what you mean. I had a chap say to me, when he found where I was from, 'how come you're a Canadian, you don't look like a Frenchman.' In Europe I puzzled the natives too. I was told that I looked like an Englishman but spoke like an American-both of which I resented. When I said I was a Canadian, he said 'it figures', or words to that effect."

"The stuffed gopher," growled Mr. Zeppelin.

"The principal characteristic of the American attitude to Canadians is warm goodwill clouded by ignorance. When you meet Americans at a convention they will say to you, all jolly and friendly, 'how's the hunting and fishing?' They seem to think Canada is a huge wildlife preserve. On the other hand, Canadians regard the States as a sanctuary for gangsters and thugs. The Canadian, after being asked how the big game season is this year and has he shot any moose, might reply, 'how's law and order these days, shot any members of the Mafia lately?'"

Mr. Zeppelin huffed appreciatively. "I'll remember that. Must do my bit for international goodwill. Another ploy is to tell an

American what a capable general you think George Washington was. When he proudly agrees with you, then say, 'he should have been, he was a well-trained British officer.' I don't recommend it though. Americans have no sense of humour about their history."

"We deplore American ignorance about Canada, but are Canadians really much more knowledgeable of the States?"

"Sure we are. Canadians are knowledgeable about all the great cultural centres of the United States-Cicero, Sausalito, the Bowery, Haight-Ashbury and San Quentin. On the other hand, an American will tell you he toured Canada once-yessiree, drove all the way from Niagara Falls to Toronto. Canadians know all the great American heroes-Al Capone, Dillinger, Hoss Cartwright and Abraham Lincoln. But if you ask an American to name three great Canadians he would probably offer Nelson Eddy and be stumped on the other two."

"In all fairness, Americans are ignorant but they mean well, they have the best of intentions."

"The most damning phrase in the English language," murmured Mr. Zeppelin.

"True. But Americans will say to you with the warmest sincerity, 'we look on Canadians as being no different from us.' Canadians resent this because they feel they are different, though just how they're not sure. But we shouldn't resent it. Americans feel they are practically perfect, so to have them say we are like them is the highest flattery they could bestow."

"Humph," grunted Mr. Zeppelin.

"I think the principal reaction of Canadians looking at America is one of fright at its immensity and power. We know they love us but we are afraid of being smothered in their embrace."

"Do you think Canada should join the United States?" I asked abruptly.

"Hell, no! We've got enough problems of our own without taking them over and straightening them out."

I laughed at his vehemence. "Canadians seem to regard the border as a sort of semipermeable membrane which keeps out the colloidal debris of the American way of life but lets in the cultural crystalloids. It works this way to some extent. At least we have control over the influx if we want to use it."

"We've got to tighten up that there membrane if we want to develop our individuality," complained Mr. Zeppelin.

I lay back and tried to picture the United States as an enormous entity. "The U.S. is a compost heap of divergent ethnic enrichments which fosters a profligate cultural growth," I suggested. "Unfortunately weeds grow as well as flowers in an enriched environment. The States lacks the maturity, judgement and courage to root out the weeds."

"Yeah, but what's weeds and what isn't?"

"Ah, a difficult question," I admitted. "One man's weed is another man's flower. At any rate I don't accept the thesis of the militant protesters who claim the ground must be sterilized and sown to salt in order to start over again. For one thing, the decision as to what to plant would remain. But, I wonder, is Canada any different?"

"Less manure, fewer weeds," suggested Mr. Zeppelin.

"Therefore easier to deal with?"

"Yes. But we have to decide soon what flowers we want in our garden and then cultivate them vigorously, rigorously and ruthlessly."

"Since money is the principal manure for our little garden, would you restrict the flow of American capital?"

Mr. Zeppelin rubbed his bald head with the flat of his hand. "We like what American money accomplishes for us but not the fact that it's their money. We're neatly on the horns of an enema."

"Well, what do you think of Canada's policy of permitting the American takeover of our natural resources?"

"Our policy on foreign ownership is like the guy with a car who couldn't afford to buy gas. He sold the car to buy the gas."

"A good analogy," I nodded.

"The Americans have squandered their resources disgracefully and now they expect us to bail them out. That is not our obbligato."

"Obbligato? Don't you mean obligation?" I asked cautiously.

"No. They expect us to play sweet harmony on a second fiddle."

"So, what's your solution?"

"We must have a bifornicated program, one for the past and one for the future. Both require long range planning, but we've got to start now or we'll be shutting the stable door after the worm has turned. First, for the future, Canadian control of all companies; no outright sales of resources; short term leases with barely enough profit allowed to be attractive and high taxes so we can use their own money to buy them out." He dusted his hands as if he had that all taken care of.

"How about the present ownership?" I asked. "Would you expropriate?"

"No. It wouldn't be honourable. Also it would dry up investment and cost Canadians their jobs. If a Canadian is going to lose his job he's honourable as hell. It is delightful when honour and self-interest coincide. A Canadian would be prepared to endure the sufferings of Canada with great heroism and fortitude, provided he doesn't have to suffer himself."

"So?"

"We can't buy back Canada overnight so we set up a long range plan to do it."

"How?"

"Issue to each Canadian paying income tax a percentage of his present tax in stock in a Canadian company, in his name and bearing nontaxable interest; if he sells he pays back taxes. This builds up a fund and gets all Canadians investing in their own country."

"Why not let the government use the money for investment?"

"Too impersonal. Also I don't want to see the government buying out and running businesses because they'd muck it up. The only enterprise a government ever made money on is selling liquor and that's a lead pipe cinch."

"All very simple," I said skeptically.

"No, not simple, but possible."

I chewed on my pen as I thought back over some of our earlier discussion. "One thing that makes a Canadian feel superior is a vague feeling that our system of government is better than the American."

Mr. Zeppelin looked at me in surprise. "Well, it is!"

"In what way?"

"Lots of ways. For one thing, how would it be if our prime minister continued in office after the House voted against him? The president does. The Canadian system is better. Out he goes, zip."

"The American system of checks and balances is rather different from our own. We-,"

"One thing for sure, American election procedures and shenanigans are a raucous absurdity. An American party convention has to be seen to be disbelieved. They're three-ringed circuses so it's no wonder Americans regard their politicians as clowns. It's things like these conventions that give democracy a bad name. Canada has retained some decorum in its election procedures which promotes respect. Our guys may be clods but they aren't clowns."

"It is true," I began "that the attitudes of Americans and Canadians to their federal governments differ. We-,"

Mr. Zeppelin cut me off. "To an American his federal government is a psychiatrist and Washington is his couch. In defence of this attitude it must be recognized that the United States has a nervous breakdown every Saturday night. To a Canadian, the federal government is a surgeon who is excising his pocketbook without an anaesthetic. The U.S. is schizophrenic; Canada is paranoid."

I laughed. "Yes, Dr. Freud."

"Freud probably enters into this somewhere. Attitudes differ towards the chief executive, too. To an American the president is the Easter bunny who will leave him a gold egg if he is a good boy; to a Canadian the prime minister is the tooth fairy-he won't get anything unless he parts with a tooth."

After delivering this broadside Mr. Zeppelin sat back and relaxed. We remained for several minutes in companionable silence. "This would appear to be a propitious moment to recharge our glasses," I suggested.

"A splendid thought," agreed Mr. Zeppelin with enthusiasm. When we had replenished our beer supply, including one for Robespierre, Mr. Zeppelin leaned back and closed his eyes. "I have a notion which has been brought to mind by our comparison of the Canadian and American personalities. It may be of help to us. I would like to cogitation it for a moment." He chewed on his mustache for several minutes. His paunch rose and fell rhythmically. I sat patiently, wondering what he was up to.

"Have you gone to sleep?" I asked politely. He opened his eyes and leaned forward.

"I have a theory on individual personalities which may be applicable on a national level," he began. "My theory is that the qualities which make an individual interesting are those which make him less likeable and admirable. The qualities which make a person lovable are gentleness, sweetness, kindness and unselfishness. But if these are all he has he is dull and a bore; a nonentity, admired but forgotten. What makes a person interesting are his quirks, whims, perversities and prejudices. In short, all those characteristics which are annoying. A person with a strong personality has them in abundance. Depending on their degree and type he may also thereby be obnoxious. Do you follow me?"

"Yes, I said. Do you think this may apply to national personalities? Is it necessary to be slightly obnoxious to establish a strong personality?"

"Possibly. Let me develop the thought." He tugged on his mustache. "If you take the nationalities with strong personalities-American, French, English, Germans, Russians-the traits which give them their individuality are those which we find annoying. They may also, of course, have likeable qualities, but what makes them stand out, and be remembered, are those attitudes which are irritating to others."

"It's an interesting theory," I said noncommittally.

"The Americans are a case in point. We have agreed that they have many likeable qualities but what gives them their striking personality is that they are bumptious, self-assertive and insensitive."

"Where does this leave Canada?"

"Out on the tundra," affirmed Mr. Zeppelin. "That's the problem. Canadians have got to give up this sweet and gentle guff and develop some barbs-not on the American plan, God forbid-but in some characteristically Canadian fashion. God damn it, Canada isn't a nation of namby-pamby, vapid nincompoops!"

"Certainly not," I agreed, squaring my shoulders. "Canada is full of virile, aggressive, debonair, cultivated men."

"True," said Mr. Zeppelin. "But subtract one from your estimate." He huffed boisterously at my look of puzzlement.

CHAPTER THREE

Punch & Judy

Our daily meetings fell more or less into a pattern with Mr. Zeppelin and his partner, Robespierre, driving up in the truck and joining me in the backyard. Robespierre always withdrew to a chair in the shade where he sipped his beer, smoked or dozed. I never did learn his real name as I am sure the title of Robespierre was one bestowed on him by Mr. Zeppelin. Our house was not on their daily schedule but they managed to arrive about the same time each day, leaving, I presume, their regular duties to wait upon their pleasure. I always had cold beer ready so we could wet our whistles before settling down to our discussions. Each day I chose a topic which we would use as a point of departure. We tended to jump around a good deal from subject to subject with frequent side trips and backtracking.

On this bright, sunny morning Mr. Zeppelin was obviously in good spirits. He tossed off his first stein of beer with his usual aplomb and wiped the froth from his mustache with an immaculate handkerchief. He was, as always, impeccably attired in grey coveralls. I suspected he managed to keep so clean by letting Robespierre do most of the dirty work. He beamed benignly at me.

"Well, what subject are we going to take a whirl at today, Professor?" he asked.

I had my plans ready. "I thought we might have a go at politics," I suggested. "I would propose that we confine ourselves initially to internal Canadian politics rather than getting into the international picture. We'll go on to that later."

"Quite so. Splendid." Mr. Zeppelin nodded happily. "If there isn't anything else I don't know more about than politics I don't know what it is. I studied politics for quite a while in the Balkans at one time and became rather proficient with a machine gun."

"Machine guns are passé in politics today."

"Not in nine-tenths of the world, my boy."

"They are in Canada, thank God, and may it always be so."

"Amen to that."

I printed "Politics" on the sheet in front of me. "The form of government which a country adopts provides an important criterion of its attitudes and therefore of its identity," I began. "The governmental structure provides the woof and warp on which the tapestry of its way of life is woven."

"Hey, that's pretty fancy. I'll buy the warped part anyhow."

"You did not disappoint me." I smiled derisively at him. "If the basic fabric is defective the pattern is distorted; if destroyed the pattern disintegrates. Canada, fortunately, has a strong fabric with which to work."

"It's getting tattered," complained Mr. Zeppelin. He blew through his mustache. "Your imagery is confusing, Professor. Yesterday flowers, today tapestries. You're mixing your semaphores."

"Metaphors," I corrected automatically.

"No, you're getting your signals crossed."

"I never learn." I threw up my hands. "Now where was I?"

"Let us deal first with some basics," I resumed. "We must accept the rudimentary premise that any society must have a set of rules with which to operate. These are established by the government, elected or imposed, of that society."

"All governments are an abomination," growled Mr. Zeppelin. "They all suppress the working man."

"Not any more they don't. They coddle and cosset him."

"No, they don't. They cozen and defraud him!"

"That's redundant."

"It sure is."

I chewed the end of my pen. "I seem to be having a difficult time keeping the ship on the rails today," I complained.

Mr. Zeppelin roared with laughter. "My, my, you are confused, Professor."

I grinned sheepishly. "I'll try again. Will you agree that some form of government is necessary?"

"I'm afraid so."

"So far so good." I bravely launched off again. "Many forms of government have been tried with varying degrees of success. A dictatorship is the most efficient but the least acceptable; democracy is the least efficient but the most acceptable. We arrive rather late in the history of man at parliamentary democracy on which the Canadian system is based. It's a cumbersome and exasperating system but the best and fairest that man has yet devised. For the working man," I added.

"The best of a bad lot," grumped Mr. Zeppelin.

"I grant that it is far from perfect in its present form but it should not, for that reason, be abandoned. We must keep the sound basic philosophy and improve the procedures."

"Don't throw out the baby with the dirty diapers, huh?" suggested Mr. Zeppelin.

"Very apt. The basic concept of a parliamentary democracy is that society elects honest men to keep the rascals in line for the good of society."

"I would submit," growled Mr. Zeppelin, "that the situation has reversed. We now elect rascals to keep honest people in line for the good of the rascals."

"Oh, come now."

Mr. Zeppelin leaned forward. "Tell me, Professor. I believe we live in the same riding. Did you vote for our present recumbent in office?"

"No."

"Why not?"

"Because he's a jackass."

"There you are." Mr. Zeppelin slumped back in his chair. "Well, he won't feel out of place in Ottawa, that's for sure."

"I realize that the antics in Ottawa are a continuing embarrassment to the Canadian people. They shouldn't be really. The brouhaha is all a necessary part of the democratic legislative fertility rites. A harmless babble which shouldn't be taken seriously. Ottawa is a sound-off spot-a combination Wailing Wall, Delphic temple, and-, and-,"

"Punch and Judy show," suggested Mr. Zeppelin.

"Right. Anyhow our boys don't compare badly with their counterparts elsewhere: the fatuity of the Americans; the twitching uncertainties of the French; the revolving door gyrations of the Italians; the vicious politeness of the British."

"How about Russia?" he asked.

"Doesn't qualify. Their presidium is a marionette show presenting 'Snow White and the Seven Dwarfs', over and over again."

"With the United States playing the part of the big bad wolf," added Mr. Zeppelin.

"Snow White doesn't have a wolf in it," I objected.

"It does in Russia."

"On the whole, our members of Parliament do pretty well when you consider what they're up against. You can't expect a shoe salesman from Lac La Biche or an underwear manufacturer from Nova Scotia, thrust suddenly into this new arena, to know anything about the complex machinery of statesmanship. This is one of the absurdities of our democratic system."

"Parliament is the only school where everybody flunks," stated Mr. Zeppelin.

"Exactly. The problem with the school is that it has no competent teachers. It's an apprenticeship system. There are really no experts in politics-only pompous pundits and cynical pragmatists."

"Well, we've got both areas covered here today," said Mr. Zeppelin with a sly grin.

"But the fact is that the system works surprisingly well," I continued. "The naivete and inexperience of the neophyte has a stabilizing effect on the aberrations of the pseudo-initiated. By the time the significance of any legislation has been drummed into the new man's thick head, it has had a pretty thorough going over. Inefficient but thorough. Stupid questions are often the best."

"Possibly, but stupid answers aren't," complained Mr. Zeppelin.

"Every new member charges off to Ottawa bright-eyed and bushy-tailed, all prepared to set the world on fire. His arrival on the scene has all the impact of a jellybean dropping into a tub of glycerin. Parliament has a quenching effect on the bizarre ideas of the uninitiated."

"And the starry-eyed theories of professors," added Mr. Zeppelin.

"Granted. And it's just as well. It would appear that all Parliament does is talk and talk and talk. Like all good Canadians I have a simple-minded faith that somewhere in behind somebody is doing something useful. There must be some machinery that is running the country, planning for the future, preparing new legislation and so forth."

"If the machinery is running the country who needs an expensive debating society? Where does your vaulted democracy fit into this?"

"Vitally and importantly," I affirmed. "The machinery-the committees, the civil service, the whatever-prepares the legislation under the direction of the party in power; but then the House has to approve it or it's no go. That's the democratic part."

"You sound like Alice in Wonderland explaining a computing centre."

"Probably," I admitted.

Mr. Zeppelin set his beer stein on top of his head. "Have another beer," I suggested.

"I thought you'd never ask," he said, helping himself to a bottle. He flipped the top off and poured the beer slowly into the stein. He raised the stein, said 'chug-a-lug', and drained it down. I was always amazed at the way he could polish off a full bottle of beer without stopping for breath. I tried it once and nearly drowned myself.

He set the stein on the grass at his feet and sat twiddling his thumbs. "A truly honest man could never get elected to Parliament," he stated flatly. "Elections are intrinsically corrupting."

"What makes you say that?"

"In order to get elected a candidate will inevitably compromise his principles. Small ways, big ways. He has to smile when he doesn't want to; say what he doesn't want to; keep quiet when he wants to speak up; be polite when he would like to spit in a guy's eye; pretend-,"

"But that's all a part of normal life," I interrupted. "All human relationships are facilitated by a sensible reticence with the truth. If we all said exactly what we think, polite social intercourse would disintegrate. What you are saying is that all life is corrupting. Which is true."

"I would agree but would submit that the pressure of corruption is intensified by any procedure which involves an election. Also elections are corrupting to the people who bring pressure on the candidate. To corrupt others is corrupting. When a candidate is elected he is conditioned to dilly-dally with the truth as he sees it. It takes a strong man to resist moral decay and a wise man to make an honourable settlement with himself."

"So it is possible to make a compromise and still be honourable?"

Mr. Zeppelin squirmed uncomfortably. "I seem to have trapped myself into that one," he admitted. "I'll say yes, by political standards."

"I would submit that politicians are more honourable than the average man, for the following reasons: one, they have more to lose if found out because they have risen above their fellows; second, in their position they are more vulnerable to the stigma of dishonesty; and third, they are above average in intelligence. It is my firm belief that dishonesty is stupid, and that intelligent people are less apt to be dishonest. I rest my case."

Mr. Zeppelin was impatient to launch a rebuttal.

"Puppy cocks," he shouted. He held up a finger.

"A," he said firmly, "they have more to lose but they have more to gain. The possibilities for skulduggery are greater and the temptation correspondingly higher; b, they are less sensitive to the stigma of dishonesty because a cynical public expects their politicians to be crooked; and c, they are below average in intelligence or they wouldn't have entered politics in the first place. But the real cruncher, Professor, is this," he slammed his hands in his knees, "many of them are lawyers." He spat out the word and glared at me. "I submit my case."

"I knew an honest lawyer once," I said quietly.

"You didn't know him very well," interjected Mr. Zeppelin bitterly.

"He worked for a union." Mr. Zeppelin glanced at me cautiously. "He lasted twenty minutes," I concluded.

Mr. Zeppelin roared with laughter. "Professor, you're as funny as a sore throat at La Scala." His good nature completely restored, he lay back happily.

"One compromise our candidate has to make right off the bat is to his party's platform, which he may like in part or not at all. This party system gives me a pain in the whoopus. Why can't you vote for the best man regardless of his party? Lots of good men don't get elected because they're running on the wrong ticket."

"You can vote for him if you want to but then you will destroy the party system," I cautioned him.

"So what?"

"The party system provides the electorate with alternative propositions."

"No, it doesn't. At least not with the propositions I want. There's no significant difference in the party platforms-just a different frosting on the same cake of soap. Anyhow, they change their platforms when they get elected, which is usually just as well."

"It's legitimate to elect a good man who is not a member of the ruling party since he can make a useful contribution as a member of the loyal Opposition," I said soothingly.

"Great balls of fire! Loyal Opposition, my foot. A loyal Opposition is like trying to empty a garbage pail with your partner pulling the opposite way. The Opposition votes against everything proposed by the party in power regardless of whether or not it's a good idea. Where's the sense in that? Even if they proposed it first and the other party stole the idea. Then if it goes through despite their best efforts they can claim credit for it if it works, and disclaim if it doesn't."

"Sure, but-,"

"The only thing the Opposition is interested in is getting back in power; just as the only concern of the party in power is to stay there. Who down there gives a damn about the poor working man?"

"All parties do, of course. They-,"

Mr. Zeppelin blew through his mustache with a powerful "pfui."

"A political party must satisfy the voter, or at least be the lesser of the evils available, in order to gain or retain power. That's legitimate surely. Parliament must have a party system so there is one group available to set up the targets for the others to shoot at. It's a bit like the advocate system in court where one lawyer-,"

"Lawyers!" roared Mr. Zeppelin. "Politics is suspect from the word go because it attracts so many lawyers. Any place lawyers congregate there's a strong aroma of fish. Lawyers!"

He stood up abruptly and reached for a beer. "I've blown up such a head of steam I'd better have a beer and simmer down." He poured out the beer and examined it lovingly. "Ah, beer that soothes the turmoil of the working man's ravelled entrails." He sipped it appreciatively.

"The politicians should be required to go pub-crawling every Saturday night. The beer parlors are the real political forums of the country. That's where they'd find out what the proletariat really thinks."

"Some politicians spend a good deal of time in bars," I commented.

"Yes, but the wrong ones. They go to cocktail lounges where they meet up with their own elks and are fortified in their bias and ignorance. They should get out into the working man's pubs where the important people congregate."

"Agreed."

"The politicians would maintain better contact with the people by going to beer parlors than to churches. For one thing more people go to beer parlors than attend church. Also the environment would be conducive to a free exchange of opinion. Minds meet in a foamy brew. People in churches are so uptight they're cutting washers." He walked back and forth. On his way he carried a beer over to Robespierre. He returned to gaze down at me.

"You and I should visit a beer parlor, Professor, to study the Canadian identity in it's native habitat. How about it?"

"I'd be delighted."

"It's a deal. I'll raise the question again later." He lowered himself into his chair and closed his eyes. "Tell me, Professor, what's the function of the Senate? I've often wondered."

I gnawed on my thumb for a moment. "Like most Canadians I don't really know. I suppose it has some use."

"Like what?"

"Well, they debate things."

"Oh, boy." He rolled his eyes. "What else?"

"It operates as a brake on legislation."

"Great balls of fire, we sure don't need that. We need an accelerator."

"The idea, I gather, is to give scrutiny to new legislation and to provide time for second thoughts."

"That would be all right if there were a chance the second thoughts would be better than the first. They won't if the Senate contributes them."

"The Senate brings, ah, maturity of judgement," I went on lamely.

"That's poop in a high wind and you know it. How mature can you get before you're dead?"

"I'm not defending the situation. I'm giving you what little I know about it. I suppose as a good Canadian I ought to look into it sometime."

"Like a typical Canadian you never will."

"Probably not," I admitted.

"How does a fellow get into the Senate?"

"They are appointed by the government, I think."

"That's like having a member of your own football team named referee."

"I guess appointment to the Senate is a substitute for knighthood more palatable to a classless society."

"It sounds like a retirement pasture for party horses, or parts thereof."

"I guess the best you can say for the Senate is that it is a silly anachronism like-," I paused, at a loss.

Mr. Zeppelin finished it for me. "Like a handpainted chamber pot left behind in the governmental commode by previous tenants?"

"Yes, that will do. Let us pass on to happier subjects. Taxes, perhaps?"

"Please. I'm going to be sick." He held his hand over his mouth.

"I gather the subject of taxes causes you distress." I smiled.

"It only hurts when I laugh."

"Have you a solution to the problem?"

"Yes, cut the taxes in half immediately."

"That would cause serious retrenchment of many programs."

"Good. Excellent. But please," he held up a hand beseechingly, "I have no stomach for the subject today. I'll have to withdraw to my room with a cup of tansy tea and a cloth soaked in witch hazel on my brow." He lay back and draped his handkerchief across his forehead.

"Very well, we'll leave that topic until you're feeling stronger. Well, how about party campaign funds. Should sources be disclosed, controlled or what?"

"Eliminated."

"Not possible."

"Then organize a sweepstake with each voter betting on his candidate. If a guy's got money riding on a political racehorse he'll take a real interest, get out and work for him and, most important of all, he'll be sure to vote."

"It would be one way to get Canadians taking a personal interest in politics I will admit."

"In any event you can't have private contributions to campaign funds. The guy that pays a prostitute expects to have first call on her services. This puts big business in the driver's seat."

"Or big unions."

"That's different."

"Like hell it is," I protested.

Mr. Zeppelin turned his hand over. "Okay, I'll accept a saw-off."

"Where do you stand on law and order?" I asked, changing the subject.

"I'm all for it. Until I get a speeding ticket."

"Typical Canadian attitude," I nodded.

"I'm all for law and odour too."

"What's law and odour?"

"Anti-pollution. Of course anti-pollution is my way of life, my profession, my raison d'etre. I looked that up. I thought it meant, 'I want to be a raisin', which seemed an odd ambition. But no Canadian contributes to pollution. Just ask one. It's always somebody else who litters or pollutes, not them. However, there's an easy solution to the problem. Make the punishment fit the grime, to paraphrase Ginsberg and Solomon. Anyone caught polluting, including presidents of big companies, should be required by the courts to go out personally to do some cleaning up. When you train a cat you rub his nose in it. He learns pretty fast; so would humans. Only in this way can we keep Canada what it is now-the most beautiful country in the world."

"I'll drink to that and throw my beer bottle over my shoulder into the ditch."

"Don't you dare." He shook his fist at me. "Come to think of it the politicians do their bit for anti-pollution."

"How do you figure that?"

"Every election they recycle a lot of garbage." He smiled at me. "And every time the House meets."

"Which is the most important leg on a tripod?" I asked abruptly.

"How's that again?"

"Law and order in a state are supported by a tripod consisting of government, judiciary and police. If any of the legs are defective the state tumbles."

"My god, not another metaphor. I can't stand it." Mr. Zeppelin held his hands to his head in mock dismay.

"Contain your enthusiasm," I admonished. "The leg of the tripod being whittled at today is the police. Canada cannot allow this to happen. The police are our thin line of defence against anarchy. Even in law-abiding Canada we have seen what happens when this defence is withdrawn. Our society must see to it that the police are supported and strengthened, not insulted, maligned and denigrated by irresponsible protesters. The police are not 'fuzz' or 'pigs.' They are our defence against tyranny. Love those cops."

"I was raised with a hairbrush, too," said Mr. Zeppelin. "I've had a bellyful, and so have most Canadians, of seeing the police abused and injured and then the do-gooders crying 'Let's not be beastly to criminals'. I say that people who break the law of the land, for whatever reason, are criminals and have to be treated as such by the courts. Please note I say by the courts. The police should not be expected nor permitted to take the law into their own hands. That is not their function."

"I agree."

"But let me be the devil's advocate here," said Mr. Zeppelin. "All these protesters mean well and are up to here with moral rectal-tube."

"Well," I said, "everyone thinks his opinions are morally sound. But society cannot permit itself to be victimized by the illegal actions of minority groups, no matter how well meaning, whether anti-war, anti-pollution, pro-drug or pro-union." Mr. Zeppelin stiffened but did not interrupt.

"The government should establish regional protest centres across the country to take the heat off the police. The centres should be manned by MPs who, after all, do have the power to change things, which the police do not. This would be a better contact with the people for the MPs than the tea parties for the anointed they presently have."

Mr. Zeppelin crossed his legs and rubbed his nose thoughtfully. "One thing we have to be thankful for," he said slowly, "is the stability of the judicial leg on your tripod. This is one area where the Canadian system has it all over the American. Their system of electing everyone from dog-catchers to sheriffs and judges is an extension of the democratic principle into areas where it doesn't work worth a damn. Surprisingly enough, our system of appointment of judges works very well indeed."

"Well, I would agree that the Canadian judiciary is almost above reproach. This is an area in which we can take pride. The respect of Canadians for their courts is a strong aspect of the Canadian identity."

"You need strong judges to keep lawyers in line," growled Mr. Zeppelin.

"Judges are lawyers," I pointed out.

Mr. Zeppelin harrumphed. "They rise superior to their regrettable antecedents."

"To pull this part of our discussion together," I stated, "I would point out that the stability of the whole structure rests with the government. Parliament makes not only the rules for the citizens of the country, but also sets the terms of reference for the judiciary and police."

"Then we are on shaky ground if we're relying on the politicians."

"No, we aren't. In a democracy, the people are the ultimate

authority and can demand and receive whatever type and degree of regulation and control of their society that they want."

"But those jackasses in Ottawa won't listen."

I smiled. "Did you know that the word 'idiot' originally meant someone who did not hold public office?"

"It's a topsy-turvy world," sighed Mr. Zeppelin sadly.

CHAPTER FOUR

Gumboot Diplomacy

The next morning, after Mr. Zeppelin had tossed off his first beer and Robespierre had retired to the shade of his favourite tree, I announced that the day's topic would be international affairs.

"Oh, good," beamed Mr. Zeppelin enthusiastically.

"As a beginning, how would you describe Canada's role on the world stage?"

"Oh, that," said Mr. Zeppelin, turning his mouth down.

"I thought you were pleased with the subject."

"I was under the impression we were going to discuss the immoral carryings-on of the Jet Set."

"No, certainly not," I said firmly. "That is not germane to the Canadian identity." Mr. Zeppelin looked so woebegone that I relented a little. "However," I went on, "I have recognized all along that we would have to come to grips sooner or later with the feminine component of our identity so-,"

Mr. Zeppelin perked up. "By all means," he said brightly, "let's come to grips with them right away." He made a huge hugging motion.

"An unfortunate choice of words. Let me rephrase my statement. What I meant-,"

"Stop toe-dancing around," said Mr. Zeppelin impatiently. "I get your point."

"Very well," I said stiffly. "What I was going to propose is that tomorrow we give consideration to the role which women play on the Canadian scene."

"Why not today? I'm hot to trot right now."

"No," I said resolutely. "I have my mind set on international affairs. I haven't been thinking about women." Mr. Zeppelin raised his eyebrows. I hurried along.

"Today we consider the international scene and tomorrow we get on to women. Damn the ambiguities of the English language! Stop raising your eyebrows at me."

"Sorry," said Mr. Zeppelin with a smirk. "I am prepared to accept your timetable," he said in a resigned tone. "Today, international affairs; tomorrow the topic which you have introduced in such a maladroit and tasteless fashion."

I fussed with my clipboard and recrossed my legs. "I shall reiterate my opening question," I snapped. "What is Canada's role on the world stage?"

"A pawn for the big powers and a patsy for the small powers," he stated promptly.

"Too simple."

"I like things simple. You can obfroniscate around all you want but that's what you'll come back to."

"Canada is widely trusted on the international scene," I said sententiously.

"We're trusted by those who figure they can bamboozle us and we aren't by the others."

"You're cynical."

"Trust everybody but always cut the deck."

I scratched my head. "We seem to be getting off to a slow start today," I complained, "let's begin again. The Canadian identity is importantly tied up with our image on the international scene. Our identity influences the image; the image may therefore give us a clue as to our identity. We can use the eyes of other nations as a mirror to catch our own reflection."

"Mirror, mirror, on the wall," intoned Mr. Zeppelin. "No, it won't work. You see in a mirror what you want to see."

"Not if you use other peoples' eyes."

"Score one for your side," conceded Mr. Zeppelin. "However, the reflection is subject to distortion."

"Of course, but it may still give us a clue. So, how do other countries see Canada?"

"As a flea on the back of the American wolf, to follow up on our earlier smelly."

"That's 'simile', as you know very well." He grinned at me without comment. "I do concede," I continued, "that Canada's foreign policy tends to ride along on the back of the United States but-,"

"You don't argue with the landlord."

"Well, ah, you have a point. But our approaches to international affairs do differ."

"Yes. Americans are frequently idiotic but never stupid; Canada is frequently stupid but never idiotic. We both have a talent for gumboot diplomacy."

"What's gumboot diplomacy?"

"On the international stage we dance *Swan Lake* in gumboots. We step on a lot of feet. The difference is that the Americans carry a fat cheque-book along with their big stick. Canadians speak loudly and carry powder puffs."

"You make more friends with a cheque-book than with a big stick," I suggested.

"I'm not so sure, if the States is taken as the example."

"Maybe not," I admitted. "The American people are the most generous and kind-hearted in the world. They are also naive, trusting and gullible. The more money they give away the more they are hated. They can't understand it. And neither can I."

"If you hand a dog a bone he will bite you. If you give him a kick in the ass he will respect you." Mr. Zeppelin paused for a moment, pulling at his mustache. "And if you do both you confuse him. A confused dog will piss on you."

I laughed. "I guess that sums up the American foreign policy paradox in a nutshell."

"For a fact."

"Where does Canada stand in this?"

"We get some of the spray."

47

I thought this over as I drew doodles on the paper on my clipboard. The doodles turned out to be small dogs and large fire hydrants. "One interesting thing about the Americans on the international scene is that they always seem to back a loser. Only once, with Israel, have they picked a winner and they're embarrassed as hell."

"Canada plays the field so we are able to offend everybody."

I decided to take a new tack. "Now you take foreign aid-," I began.

"I won't but there's no shortage of people lined up with their hands out."

"I feel that the programs of the western nations in making financial aid available to those less fortunate is one of the finest examples of generosity the world has ever seen."

"The swing of a moral pendulum," intoned Mr. Zeppelin. "In the early days the whites exploited the coloured peoples, but now the undernourished countries are exploiting the whites by moral blackmail—justified, it is true. The whites are paying off on a guilty conscience which they pretend is humanity. Once the debt has been balanced the whites will get fed up and call it quits."

"The debt can never be balanced," I affirmed vigorously. "How can we ever give recompense for centuries of vicious repression?"

"We can't. That's the point. The West cannot and will not destroy itself trying. But before they go financially bankrupt they will go morally bankrupt. As I say, they will call it quits. Furthermore, a nation has a first responsibility to look after its own citizens."

"Well, I think the affluent nations, including Canada, have a continuing moral obligation to help the 'have-not' nations."

"Well, I think our country has a moral obligation to help its own people first," he said. "Until every Canadian is receiving a respectable living wage I don't see why we should provide gifts to a camel driver in East Wallabubu."

"Are you a racist then?"

"Certainly not. I don't care whether a guy's brown, black, green or purple, or what country he's from. But I say Canadians should look after Canadians first. This giveaway money comes out of the working man's pocket, you know. He'd rather see it used to help our Indians, Eskimos and poor people. If the government would put these foreign aid bills to a plebiscite they wouldn't pass, I can tell you. Not until every Canadian was employed and earning a living wage. Then the bill would pass and happily."

"But the 'have-not' nations are in worse shape than we are."

"Why are they 'have-not' nations?"

"Because they haven't our resources and are overpopulated and-,"

"Why are they overpopulated?"

"Well, for obvious reasons."

"You betcha. I say foreign aid should be tied to the pill, fifty-fifty. Half for food and economic help and half for the pill. If they won't accept and use the pill, then to hell with them. Otherwise you're pouring water down a gopher hole. They just have more kids and you're back where you started-not enough food. It's the old Methuselah principle."

"I agree that the underdeveloped nations must assume more responsibility for their population growth. There's no way western agricultural technology can keep up with the copulatory irre-sponsibility of the otherwise non-productive nations. The salvation of the world rests with the pharmaceutical industry, not the agri-cultural departments."

"Right. And the Canadian taxpayer doesn't want to get screwed every time a guy in Rabistan unzips his burnous. That's what the boys in my non-exclusive club, the beer parlor, say. And I'll bet the boys in the taverns in Sanfranpennsyldelphia say the same thing."

"I suppose they do," I admitted.

"Another thing," Mr. Zeppelin continued vehemently, "when we're giving money to other nations it should be given to the work-ing men, not the bloody politicians. They line their own pockets first and then buy guns and tanks. Every emerging nation today has a bunch of bums running it who feel they have to have a big army. This is for prestige and to keep their own people subjected. If the working man was given the help he'd put it to sensible use, you can be sure. Also if we can help a man help himself then he keeps his dignity, he doesn't feel he's a panhandler."

"I agree with that if it can be implemented."

"Sure it can. When I go to borrow money at the bank I don't get it if I'm going to use it foolishly."

"Go on," I interjected, "banks would go out of business if they stopped lending money for foolish enterprises. However, I agree with you in your contention that the poor countries spend an idiotically and tragically high proportion of their meagre resources on armaments."

"Including Canada," growled Mr. Zeppelin. "Who needs armed rowboats?"

"Everyone arms for defence-no one for offence-so who needs weapons? The developed nations are to blame for the problem because they sell the weapons."

"Right," said Mr. Zeppelin.

"Most of the developing countries are overcrowded," I continued. "Should not an increasing number of these people be brought into the advanced nations? Or are you opposed to immigration?"

"By no means. Provided," he held up his finger. "Provided, they don't take jobs away from Canadians. Also provided they can be assimilated into the work force and are prepared to work. I am not about to see them come over here to sit on their fadoos."

"Canada is one of the less densely populated areas of the world. I feel we have a moral duty to permit those from congested areas to enter freely and fill up our great open spaces."

"It doesn't work that way," complained Mr. Zeppelin. "If you allow people to enter freely they don't fill up the empty places. They clutter up the already congested areas. You don't find any of them out on a stubble ranch in Saskatchewan or up in the Northwest Territories. No sir, you find them on the dole in Toronto, or Montreal or Vancouver. And the dole, I would add, is provided by the Canadian working man. Also they expect instant affluence without working for it."

"Some people would say you are disclosing a bit of bigotry."

Mr. Zeppelin shrugged. "Maybe just a touch of bigotry is part of the Canadian identity."

I was startled at the thought. This had not occurred to me. "Maybe it is," I said slowly.

Mr. Zeppelin stood up and stretched. "I've been sounding off so much I could spit philosophy." He helped himself to a beer and handed me one. "What have you got on that sheet of paper out of all this?" he asked.

I held it up. "Some fine sketches of dogs and hydrants."

"Excellent. Sums things up very nicely." He returned to his chair.

"Speaking of the relationships of diverse nations," I said, "where do you stand on the British Commonwealth?"

"Your turn. You lead off."

"All right. My own feeling is that the Commonwealth served a useful purpose at one time but is now an anachronism. England is now a mother hen with all her chicks tugging at the lease."

"I think you mixed up another one of those things, Professor."

"And some of the chicks have turned out to be cuckoos in the nest."

"Better and mixder," he chortled.

"The relationships within the Commonwealth countries nicely epitomize the dilemma between the advanced and the developing nations on a global scale."

"Yes, the 'have-nots' of the Commonwealth will get such conscience money as they can from the others and will then politely withdraw. There will be left those who have something in common-Britain, Canada, New Zealand and Australia. And Ireland."

"Ireland?" I cried in surprise.

"Yes. Ireland will become part of Britain again. It makes sense." He nodded solemnly.

"Sense has no place in Irish politics for Pete's sake."

"Regrettably true. But Ireland will return to Britain via the European Economic Community."

"I should live so long."

"You won't but it will happen."

"Then I can't prove you wrong. How about the United States? Will they return to the fold?"

"No, although they would like to. The Americans would love to be part of a monarchy although they would vociferously deny it. A monarchy lends itself to snobbery for those so inclined and the Americans are the biggest snobs on earth. That's why they keep deifying tinsel broads to pay homage to. Their temporary begums always let them down by silly or venal piccadillos in or out of wedlock. So they coronate a new one with the same results. Canada is their envy because we have a lovely and gracious lady as queen who is top flight, top drawer and, I suppose you could use the expression, the real McCoy."

"Do I gather from your comments that you are in favour of a monarchy for Canada?"

"Yes, indeed. The monarchy gives a bit of class to our classless society. Mind you, I'd be strongly opposed if we had in Canada a hierarchy usually associated with a monarch, such as dukes, earls, barons, counts, no-accounts and all that sort of balderdash. Canadians wouldn't put up with it. But the way it is now with all Canadians supposedly equal and then, zip," he moved his hand quickly in an upward stroke, "to one supreme figurehead, that's fine."

"I'm glad to hear you say so," I said in some surprise.

"Another thing. Democracy tends to be unstable due to the shifting whims of the proletariat. A constitutional monarchy provides stability. The crown's an anchor. This wasn't always so. In the old days, everyone wanted to be king so there was a good deal of competition for the job which led to sanguinary ruckuses. But nowadays the job isn't all that attractive so if you've got some conscientious family stuck with it, then you tend to have stability and continuity."

"Yes, why would anyone want to be a monarch today?"

"Yeah, it's not all that prestigimous a job either as they only have it by the sufferance of the working classes. It's too bad, though, that the Queen has an English accent."

"Why, for heaven's sake?"

Mr. Zeppelin scratched his chin. "Well, the English accent rubs Canadians the wrong way. It gets their dandruff up. Any other accent is all right-Scottish, Ukrainian, Norwegian or what have you-but the English accent always sounds affected, not to mention condescending. I don't know why that is."

"Maybe they intend it that way."

"Possibly. The English accent is a funny thing in that it sounds so prim and proper. Even when an English bird is panting amorous pleasantries in your ear she sounds like the Archbishop of Whiffle-tree saying grace. It turns a guy off."

I laughed. "Surely not."

"Anyhow, the reaction of Canadians to the Queen is confused by their reaction to the English, which isn't all that favourable. There's still a little of the 'no Englishman need apply' mentality remaining. To be brutally frank, Canadians find Englishmen a bit of a pain in the ass."

"Why?"

"You know that G.B. on the back of English cars? It stands for God's Beloved."

"Oh, it does not."

Mr. Zeppelin held a conspiratorial finger to his lips. "Did you know that Narcissus was a Rhodes scholar?"

I laughed. "Everybody makes fun of the English for being English. They even kid themselves about it."

"Yeah, but their hearts aren't in it. They're just being polite. The English are always polite. It's their way of being annoying. Also it's a defence mechanism more impervious than chain mail."

"Nonsense," I objected, "there's nothing wrong with being polite."

"Not if you mean it. When a Canadian is polite he does it on purpose; when an Englishman is polite it's a defensive reflex. Never try to out-polite an Englishman. For one thing it can't be done and if you try you will end up wallowing around in treacle. An Englishman can politely trample you underfoot."

"I don't believe a word of it."

"Well, anyhow," Mr. Zeppelin sounded plaintive. "I sure wish the Queen would take some elocution lessons and learn to talk properly-like a Canadian."

CHAPTER FIVE

Sugar and Spice and Sports

Next morning Mr. Zeppelin arrived, a flower pinned to his tunic.

"Since we are going to be discussing women this morning," he explained, "I thought it appropriate to doll up a bit. I brought you one too. I found them in a trash can up the alley." With considerable ceremony he pinned a wilted gardenia on my shirt. He stepped back to admire his handiwork. He looked disappointed.

"You need pennies on your eyes to complete the picture," he sighed. "Ah well." He helped himself to a beer and handed one to a grinning Robespierre, who was wearing a huge droopy chrysanthemum on his chest.

"You look beautiful, Robespierre," I said.

"Thanks," he answered with a happy smile, fluffing his flower. We settled down in our usual chairs.

"It may seem disgraceful that two old roués like us should be dissecting the flower of Canadian womanhood," I began.

"We'll treat them with tender loving care," he interjected. "They couldn't be in better or kinder hands."

We were interrupted by a great din in the back alley. I looked up in surprise. Two huge garbage trucks came along to park behind Mr. Zeppelin's truck.

"Oh, I forgot to mention, Professor," he said, "that I invited some of the boys to join us today. I was telling them at headquarters what you and I have been trying to do in establishing the great Canadian identity and I mentioned that today we were going to be discussing women. Some of them asked if they could come along and I said sure. Is that all right?"

"Why, certainly," I said. "They would be very welcome. I had no idea there was such an interest in the Canadian identity."

Mr. Zeppelin laughed. "There is in the component we are dealing with today."

While we were talking, two more trucks appeared and parked behind the others. It looked as if we had the entire sanitation department in our alley. The men descended from their cabs and ambled over to the fence wearing broad grins.

"Come on in, boys," shouted Mr. Zeppelin. "The Professor says he would be delighted to have you join us for our deliberations on the uncharitable sex."

I added my welcome as the men trouped into the yard and then dashed into the house for more beer, taking Robespierre along as an assistant. We carried out three cartons which we set on a lawn table. Robespierre served happily as bartender, providing each of the visitors with a bottle, after which they sat or lay on the lawn in a semicircle facing Mr. Zeppelin and myself.

There was a good deal of good-natured banter with Mr. Zeppelin, who was obviously enjoying himself thoroughly. As he introduced me to each of the men, they acknowledged the introduction with a wave of the beer bottle. I was unable to remember all of the names, but I did manage to identify Oscar, a thin, intense man with sharp, intelligent eyes sitting directly in front of me; Rory, a husky redhead with a freckled face sitting off to the right; and Zack, a grey-haired, older chap with a swarthy, heavily lined face. The men ranged in age from early twenties to late fifties and appeared to represent a variety of ethnic origins. Their clothes were a nondescript assortment of overalls, sweaters, sports shirts and ragged jackets. They were a happy, delightful group.

As I picked up my clipboard they fell silent. I was the centre of attention of ten pairs of inquisitive, speculative eyes. It was challenging and somewhat disconcerting. I cleared my throat.

"Well, gentlemen," I began, "I am delighted that you have been able to take time from your busy schedules to join us in our discussions today. As I believe Mr. Zeppelin has told you, he and I have been endeavouring to delineate the Canadian identity; that is, to determine what constitutes a Canadian, in his own eyes and in the eyes of the world. Our subject today is the Canadian woman." There was some shuffling and elbow nudging.

"We are fortunate to have such a splendid cross section of Canadian, ah, chivalry here, so we should be able to emerge from our deliberations with a valid concensus. Since women constitute over half the Canadian population-,"

"Women live longer than men," explained Mr. Zeppelin. "They do it on purpose, too."

I ignored this. "It is essential that we explore their contribution to the Canadian identity."

"I think this class should have a lab, Professor," called someone.

"Restrain your enthusiasm, gentlemen," I admonished. "Our researches are in the interests of science, not of revelry."

"Pity," grumped Mr. Zeppelin. There was a chorus of boos.

It was apparent that Mr. Zeppelin considered himself more or less the co-chairman of the meeting. He had a tendency to play up to the audience by interpolations and ribald comment, which was probably fortunate since it put the men at ease and helped to ameliorate my rather pedantic approach.

I continued. "The first thing we must accept, gentlemen, is the fact that women are different from men."

"Now there's a profound statement if I ever heard one," said Mr. Zeppelin with a whack of his hand on his knee.

"You've been peeking, Professor," called someone.

I felt my face reddening. "I was not referring to ah, anatomical differences, although they exist, of course," I floundered.

"A university education is a wonderful thing," said Mr. Zeppelin solemnly.

"What I was addressing our attention to is the fact that women have a different chemistry which influences their physiological and psychological responses. There is a complex interreaction of hormonal factors from the pituitary, gonads and other endocrine glands, notably the estrogens and androgens, which-,"

"Whoa up there, Professor, you left me behind on that bit," said Oscar.

"Just remember Ester is a girl and Andy is a boy," I suggested.

Oscar and the others still looked puzzled. I thought for a moment.

"I know what I'll do. Let the meeting be at ease. I shall return in a moment with some props." I hastily brought from the house some wall charts which I had prepared for a refresher course. I hung these on the clothesline and, using a rake for a pointer, gave a dissertation on the chemistry of estrogens and androgens and their effects on secondary sex organs and characteristics. The interest and attentiveness of my audience led me to wish I could elicit such response from my university classes.

I continued with a brief summary of the genetic factors in sex determination with emphasis on the XX and XY chromosomes. Rory found significance in the fact that the female was characterized by a double cross.

As I finished my discourse, I became aware that my neighbour, Jack Peters, was leaning across the fence, a look of wonderment on his round, cheerful face. "What the hell's going on?" he asked.

"We're discussing women," I explained.

"My favourite opposite sex," said Jack. "May I join you?"

"I doubt if you know anything about the subject," I said, "but sure, come on over. You might learn something that would surprise Agnes. Pull up a blade of grass and sit down."

Jack clambered over the fence, helped himself to a beer and joined the circle.

"I thought maybe you had precipitated a crisis in the sanitation division," he said, "by throwing out all your empties at one time." I introduced Jack to the group with a wave of the hand.

"This is my nosey neighbour, Jack Peters, who borrows my lawnmower and trains his dog to do his doings on my side of the fence. Jack, meet the Eightieth Avenue Brownie Pack." The men all said 'hi' and raised their bottles in greeting.

I returned to the discussion. "Now that we have covered some basics, class, er, I mean, gentlemen, let us proceed to an evaluation of the contribution of Canadian women to our identity. First of all, what kind of fauna are we dealing with here; what are their characteristics; what are their attributes? I shall begin with a provocative opening statement which you may challenge, modify or agree with." I paused dramatically.

"It is my opinion, after giving considerable study to the subject, that Canadian women are the most beautiful in the world."

Mr. Zeppelin held up his stein. "Hear, hear. I'll drink to that." Most of the others joined him with enthusiastic 'hear, hears'. Mr. Zeppelin whispered a loud aside behind his hand, "His wife's listening at the window."

"While there are undoubtedly lovely women elsewhere in the world," I continued, "for overall pulchritudinous qualifications, give me a Canadian woman every time."

"Yeah, give me one, too," said a voice. There was another chorus of 'hear, hear'.

"Try to be constructive," I complained. "I need help, not a cheering section."

"You need help, all right, Professor," said Mr. Zeppelin. "You may be big on book learning, but chemistry cuts no hay in a wild oats patch."

"Yes, it does, but we'll let that go for the moment. I've heard no one with the temerity to refute my thesis that for beauty of form and face the Canadian woman has it all over her competition elsewhere."

"I think you are right, Professor," said Rory, "but why is that so? All the Canadian gals come from other countries or their folks did."

"I would submit," I answered, "that Canadian girls take on a personality and a lustre of their own, quite distinct from their origins."

"I agree with the Professor," said someone. "Second generation girls have a beauty their mothers never had. I don't know why. But they lengthen out, slim down and smarten up so it is a wonderful thing." Others agreed with this analysis.

"I believe we are on sound ground in maintaining that Canadian girls are different from their counterparts elsewhere," said Mr. Zeppelin. "For example, the Montreal girls are superb and have it all over their French analogues like a tent. They have retained the sophisticated Parisienne chic yet have superimposed a vibrance and freshness not seen in a more effete milieu."

"How about the Oriental gals, Zep?" called someone.

Mr. Zeppelin kissed his fingertips. "The Canadian girls of oriental background are entrancing. The mystery of the Orient, the charm of exotic lands combined with Canadian pizzaz makes a delightful combination. They are a splendid example of what the Professor said about girls from other countries super-blooming in Canada and taking on a special Canadian effulgence."

"How about the Indian girls?" asked a young chap, whose black hair and high cheekbones bespoke more than a casual interest.

"As beautiful as any," declaimed Mr. Zeppelin. "The raven hair, the beguiling brown eyes, the stillness of the forest, the softness of midnight. Ah, superb. But beauty requires an appropriate environment to do it justice. A flower is enhanced by a crystal vase; a diamond deserves a Tiffany setting. Too often our stupid society has not provided a worthy setting for our Indian maidens. But they are lovely notwithstanding and can stand proudly with the most comely."

"You know it's true what the Professor said," commented Rory. "I've travelled around the world quite a bit and the Canadian girls are prettier and, uh, nicer than their cousins who stayed behind. For one thing, foreign girls are often too fat for Canadian tastes."

"A fat woman is just too much of a good thing," stated someone.

"It all depends," said Mr. Zeppelin enigmatically.

"Obesity has ruined more marriages than adultery," murmured Jack Peters.

As this did not appear to be a particularly useful area of discussion I interrupted.

"One problem Mr. Zeppelin and I have had in establishing the Canadian identity," I said, "is distinguishing ourselves from the Americans. Do you think that Canadian women are significantly different from their American counterparts?"

"You'd better believe it," said a voice.

"You're damn tooting," said someone else.

"You ever bite into a luscious cherry and crack your tooth on the pit? That's the American dame for you," stated Rory. Others nodded.

"American women have voices you could scratch a match on," said someone.

"American dames are awful bossy of their menfolk," observed Rory. "Canadian gals are more subtle like."

"It has been claimed," I said, "that the States operates under a tyrannical uxorocracy and-,"

"Whatever that is," interrupted Mr. Zeppelin, "is Canada really any different?"

"Yes, in that the American male knows he's a serf, but the Canadian male thinks he's king of his castle."

"Would you accept 'cock of the walk'?" asked Jack Peters.

I ignored the suggestion. "This doesn't prove he is, because he isn't but it does prove that the Canadian female is smarter than the American female in that she is wise enough to foster a kindly delusion."

"Real kindness in a dame is rare, as rare as a betrothal in a brothel," contributed Mr. Zeppelin.

"We seem to be generally agreed," said Jack Peters, "that the Canadian woman is a wonderful creature. The question then arises, is the Canadian male up to the challenge imposed thereby?"

"A good point," nodded Mr. Zeppelin. "A Stradanervous violin deserves a master's touch."

"You should meet my ukulele," said someone.

A vigorous discussion ensued on the virtues of the Canadian male which left no doubt that the group felt that all manly responsibilities could be adequately met.

"Your response, gentlemen," I commented, "is highly creditable to the Canadian woman in that it is apparent she has convinced the Canadian male he is a paragon. However, we have not really come to grips with our objective. We have established that Canadian women are beautiful and charming, but I suggest that they are more than sugar and spice and everything nice. What do they contribute to the Canadian identity beyond being ornamental?"

"Ain't that enough?" asked Rory.

"No," I answered. "And it certainly doesn't tell the whole story."

"It sure as hell don't," agreed Zack. "It's really the women that give Canada its identity. The men strut and bow on the stage but it's the women who keep the show on the road. When you establish what the Canadian identity is, Professor, you'll find that women are a real important part of it, and contribute practically all the part that's creditable."

"I was hoping we could get at it the other way," I explained. "That is, establish the female component of our identity and then add that to other parameters so we could come up with a total picture."

Zack tugged at his ear. "It ain't that easy. Establishing the female component of our identity is just as tough as finding our total identity. It's all tied in together. But I say Canada is as great as the women in it. So we're in damn good shape." Oscar snorted. Zack glared at him.

"I mean it. When the explorers first came to this country they had a high old time, travelling around, seeing new, exciting things, shooting buffalo and all that stuff. They were happy to carry on like that. It wasn't until the women came that civilization arrived. Women are braver and more daring than men. Men wouldn't have the guts to set up housekeeping out in the wilderness unless it had a big stockade around it. But the women weren't afraid. It takes a lot of courage to go out in the wilds and establish a home and raise kids and so forth. This country was settled by the women with the men tagging along behind and don't you think otherwise."

"Hell, Zack," objected Rory. "That was two hundred years ago. Things are different now."

"No, they ain't. Not basically. Women still have more guts than men when it comes to trying new things and they're still trying to civilize us apes. Hell, my wife had to carry me to my first symphony concert and now I like it just fine. I'm old fashioned enough to think the family is pretty important. Kids are as good as the family they come out of and a family's as good as the mother in it. So, like I say, Canada's in good shape." A pensive silence followed.

"Now would appear to be a good moment to adjourn the meeting briefly to enable you to recharge your glasses," I offered.

"Good idea," said Mr. Zeppelin. "Robespierre," he roared, "bestir yourself. See to it that our guests are provided with adequate libations."

Robespierre, with Jack Peters' assistance, brought everyone a fresh bottle. When this service had been completed, I brought the meeting back to order.

"I propose now, gentlemen," I began, "to turn the searchlight of your scrutiny on the women's liberation movement. It is interesting to note that the glorification of Canadian womanhood which we have indulged in so far this morning, would be resented by women's lib as maintaining women as sex symbols and house pets. Zack has made an eloquent and, I feel, completely valid tribute to Canadian womanhood's contribution to our way of life. However, he has confined his remarks largely to the traditional and stereotyped role of women in society. They are no longer prepared to confine themselves to this function; they wish to get out into the world to do important things on an equal basis with men. I would submit that this is reasonable and inevitable."

Mr. Zeppelin growled, "Women's lib uses a cactus plant for a powder puff. The silly things."

I was surprised. "Don't you believe in the emancipation of women?"

Oscar spoke up. "They're emancipated all to hell and out the other end already. The dames got the world by the tail now, so why should they want to change things? For their own sake they shouldn't be taken seriously."

"Running a home and raising the kids is an important job," stated someone. "If you think raising kids these days ain't a full-time job you ain't in touch."

"But women want more than that," I objected. "They want the

challenge of life outside the home, in business, the professions and so forth."

"Woman's place is in the boudoir," growled Mr. Zeppelin.

"Women's lib would say you are a chauvinistic, reactionary misogynist," I said.

"Is that good?"

"No."

"It sounded nice." He shrugged.

"There's enough unemployment now without the dames getting jobs and making it worse," said Rory. Several others agreed.

"They're doing okay now, so why make a federal case out of it?" asked Oscar.

"Surely, gentlemen," I said, "you would feel that women should have an equal status with men and should compete on an equal basis. How many of you have wives who are working?" About half of them held up their hands. "There you are," I said. "Don't you feel that the working woman should be well paid and remunerated on an equal basis with men for the same work?"

In the discussion which followed, it appeared that most of the men deplored the economic necessity for working wives although they agreed that women should have equal pay for equal work. Most of them felt that the present set-up gave ample scope for women.

"Hell," observed someone, "if a dame's got ability she can find a job doing what she's good at. As Oscar says, why make a big thing out of it?"

"Women's lib says women are repressed and exploited," I pressed. "They want women to be released from the restrictions which have held them in for centuries. Surely you would accord them this freedom? How about politics? Shouldn't there be more women in politics? Women are more realistic and hard-headed than men as well as being more intuitive."

"A woman's intuition is the means by which she arrives at the wrong conclusion without the use of the fallacious reasoning she would otherwise use to arrive at the wrong conclusion," commented Mr. Zeppelin. "I read that somewhere." He grinned at me wickedly.

The ensuing discussion revealed the feeling that nearly anything would improve the political situation-even the participation of women. There was a good deal of sympathy for the objectives of the women's liberation movement, but not for the movement per se. Women's lib was described as everything from petulant whimsy (Jack) and perverse buffoonery (Mr. Zeppelin) to

a pile of horseshit (Oscar). The leadership and methods of operation came under scathing criticism. Someone claimed that the
leaders were a group of shrews more interested in puffing
themselves up than in the aims of the movement. I objected without
much success.

"The trouble is," said Oscar, "these dames see themselves
sitting behind a big desk ordering men around. That's their
personal objective. They sure as hell don't see themselves taking
orders."

"I think," said Mr. Zeppelin thoughtfully, "that men can learn to
function satisfactorily under a competent female executive. But
where the fit hits the shan is when dames try to boss other dames.
I remember when I was coach of a girls' hockey team in Sumatra-,"

"Hockey in Sumatra?" I asked.

"Grass hockey." He gave me a condescending look. "When I quit
they got a female coach. She lasted two days before one of the girls
laid her out with a wallop on the noggin with a hockey stick."

"Zep's right," affirmed Rory. "Broads don't trust other broads.
There's enough female voters in Canada to elect any dame they
want right now but they don't. They elect men."

"More women should be encouraged to run for public office,"
I insisted.

"The dames won't vote for them if they do," said Rory. "You
can't change human nature and in some respects dames are
human."

"These dames who want to liberate women," said someone,
"ought to go to the country I come from and see what it's like where
women really got to work. It's cruel what hard work does to a
woman. That's the main reason we like Canada. A woman can be
a woman."

"The trouble with Women's lib is they got no sense of humour,"
said Rory.

"Dames don't have a sense of humour, period," said Mr. Zeppelin. "One of the characteristics of a sense of humour is that you
can see your own absurdity. Dames never see themselves as
absurd, even when they are, or more particularly, especially when
the are-which is most of the time."

"We seem to be wandering from the subject," I complained. "Do
you not see a more meaningful partnership developing between
husband and wife as the wife participates more fully in the life of
the community?"

"Behind every successful man stands a woman, surprised as
hell," said Oscar. "And behind every unsuccessful man stands a

woman saying, 'I told you so, and mother agrees'."

"That isn't a partnership," I objected.

"The only good thing about marriage is you ain't lonely," stated Oscar. "Loneliness is worse than unhappiness. That's the only excuse for marriage."

"I don't buy that," objected Rory. "I still believe in, ah, romance."

Mr. Zeppelin huffed. "Romantic love is a myth initiated by unmarried poets and fostered by florists."

"To get this show back on the road," I complained. "I am still trying to find whether or not Women's lib has a useful job to do in developing an expanded role for the Canadian woman."

"No," said Oscar flatly. "Somebody called them a group of braless bubbleheads, and that about sums it up. Look at some of the things they've done. They've promoted this Ms. nonsense and I can't even pronounce it. Their insistence on job equality has fouled up job advertising like you wouldn't believe. You can't even advertise for a garbageman today. You'd have to call it a garbage person. I wonder where you could list a job for a wet-nurse."

Zack leaned forward earnestly. "I've been listening to all the furor here for the last while and I ain't heard much sensible objection to the women getting out and getting involved. It's just how they're going about it that's a pain. Let them do their thing, as the kids say. I think our reaction to women is much like our reaction to Quebec-do what you want to do as long as you don't destroy our happy home." Zack glared around at the group. Some of the men nodded in agreement while others looked highly sceptical.

"I'll buy all that," said Rory with a wave of the hand. "But say, Professor, to change the subject a little, have you done anything on the role of sports in the Canadian identity?"

"No, we haven't so far. But I don't feel we've really completed our studies on the Canadian woman yet."

"Oh, sure we have. Let's get on to something important. A woman is only a woman but a good forward pass is a zinger." He went through the motions of throwing a football.

"Rory was third substitute waterboy for the Stampeders ten years ago and he's been an authority on sports ever since," growled Mr. Zeppelin. "When he ran on the field at half-time with his water bucket he was given a standing ovation, to hear him tell it."

Rory made a rude gesture in Mr. Zeppelin's direction. "Sports accomplishes more for the Canadian identity than anything else there is. You take that Canada-Russia hockey series. It did more to pull Canada together than the CNR and CPR combined. Fourteen million Canadians watched those games and any time you get that many Canadians pulling the same way at the same time it's got to be a powerful uniting force. Hockey is a very special thing to Canadians. It's our national game and I'd say it comes closest to representing our Canadian identity than anything else you can think of."

"Yeah," said Zack. "Did you hear the way those guys there sang *O Canada*? It was really something. Made you realize all of a sudden that it's a wonderful thing to be a Canadian. It took hockey to bring that out. And when we won I nearly split a gut. So did all of Canada."

"We damned near blew it," said Oscar. "Them Russkies scared hell out of us. One thing we learned, I hope, is you don't win games sitting in the penalty box. In international affairs, if you're going to be dirty, you've got to be sneaky."

"The scare may do us good," suggested Rory. "It shows we've got to improve our organization, our training and coaching, right down to the pee-wee level. We've got to encourage and support the kids all the way along the line, right up to athletic scholarships at universities so they have some options open to them. Right now we've still got a slave system, although it's a little better with the expansion and two pro leagues. But as soon as the pro leagues combine, and they will sooner or later, we'll be back to a monopoly."

"The only thing expansion has done," complained Oscar, "is to dilute the game so that now even the Americans can play it."

"One big advantage of the expansion," said Zack, "is that the competition has zipped the salaries away up. That's good. I like to see the players getting more of the sugar instead of the goddamned promoters."

"A good slap-shot is worth more than a Ph.D. these days," said Mr. Zeppelin with a sideways grin at me.

"Nolle prosequi," I conceded.

"The next time Canada plays Russia-," began Rory.

"What makes you think there'll be a next time?" interrupted Jack Peters.

"Of course there will," answered Rory in surprise. "International hockey is here to stay."

"You're right," said Jack. "But it may be under a new format where the team won't represent Canada. I agreed with you when you said hockey comes close to representing the Canadian identity. It does so also in a less happy sense in that it is completely dominated by the States. The NHL has a strangle hold on all hockey in Canada, including Team Canada. I need hardly point out that the NHL is controlled by American interests who don't give a damn about Canada beyond being a provider of talent. International hockey will be heavy sugar and the NHL will want to be in on it. That won't necessarily mean sending a team representing Canada. If you don't think they have control, look at the way they were able to prevent Hull from playing."

"That was skullduggery of a high odour," grumped Mr. Zeppelin.

"The only way I can see that we can keep our best players in Canada," continued Jack, "is to do what Brazil did when Pelé was flirting with playing for a foreign country-they declared him a national treasure which therefore could not be exported. I think we should declare Hull, Esposito and Orr and some of the other boys as national monuments."

"It won't work," complained Zack. "Canada is busy selling off all its national treasures to the Yanks."

"I'm afraid you're right," conceded Jack. "But interestingly enough the Hull affair alerted Canadians to the degree of domination of Canada by the Americans. When a foreign power can prevent a Canadian, belonging to a Canadian club, from playing on the national team, then this brings home to everybody the degree of our subservience. The average guy either doesn't understand or doesn't care about American take-over of our resources and economy but he can sure as hell recognize the heavy American hand on our athletes."

"The Yanks might get even with us by preventing their football players from coming up here," commented someone.

"That would be just fine," stated Rory vehemently. "Canadian football right now is dominated by American players and coaches. As a result, the Grey Cup, our great national sports spectacle, is a sham. What do you see there? A group of overpaid Americans, with a sprinkling of underpaid Canadians, competing for a Canadian trophy. The whole show is about as Canadian as Imperial Oil or Canada Safeway."

There were several violent objections to his thesis. The Grey Cup was held to be a truly Canadian spectacle which served as a great unifying phenomenon each fall. The fact that Americans were involved was considered by most of the men as immaterial since it was a professional league. There was general agreement, however, that Canadian football talent should be developed and promoted, though just how was not clear.

"Curling, at any rate, will continue to be uniquely Canadian," observed Zack. "There ain't enough bucks in it to attract the Yanks. But if it ever gets to be a money maker they'll move in on it, too."

The virtues of curling were extolled by several others; Canada's prominence in the sport was viewed with pride and satisfaction. It was felt that curling throughout Canada all winter, culminating in the Brier, provided a common bond for Canadians which pulled all the provinces together in fraternal concord.

The conversation took a sudden shift to a discussion of hunting, fishing and from that to the broader aspects of other outdoor sports including camping, canoeing, skiing and swimming. In response to a few judicious enquiries from me, it was agreed that a love of the outdoors was a characteristic Canadian trait.

"I just like to get out and commute with nature," stated Rory. "Just sit under a pine tree and talk to the sassy chipmunks. I just love chipmunks."

"Are female chipmunks called chipnuns?" asked Mr. Zeppelin.

Rory ignored the question. He went on to complain about the increased cost of resort areas and the crowded facilities. "With our short summer," he said, "and everybody and his dog out in the parks it's getting so you can hardly turn around without bumping into somebody."

"It's getting so there ain't no place for our wild animals to live with any happiness," complained someone.

"Yeah," agreed another voice. "You've got to go farther and farther out in the bush to get any good hunting."

"I think hunting ought to be abolished anyhow," stated Zack firmly. "How anybody can go out and slaughter our magnificent wild creatures and call it sport I'll never know."

"I agree," I stated. "What's sporting or manly about using a small cannon with a telescopic lens to shoot down an unsuspecting animal a half mile away? I like watching chipmunks too, along with Rory, but do you want to shoot them?" Rory looked startled and shook his head.

"No. It wouldn't be sporting. I say it isn't any more sporting to kill a moose, or a grizzly, or a lynx. Anybody who would kill a polar bear in the name of sport has to be a sadistic freak. A daffodil is a beautiful creature of nature too, but nobody, as far as I know, goes shooting them. The animals in their own way are just as beautiful and helpless. Leave them alone."

"I just wish I had enough dough to buy up a big tract of land and let the game live there in peace," said Zack. "But hell, it's getting so an average Canadian can't afford to buy even a tiny plot of land unless he goes north of the Arctic Circle."

"You know why that is?" stated Rory. "Our friends to the south know a good thing when they see it. You try to buy a lot on Lake

Erie and find out who owns it. The Americans already own a high percentage of our islands and coastline and a lot of lake-front properties all over the country. It's a scandal that's what it is. And the governments ain't doing a damn thing about it. The prices go up and up; it's no wonder a Canadian can't afford to buy any property. How the hell are we going to stop it and recover the land we've lost?"

"The only way Canadians are going to regain ownership of their own land and resources," said Mr. Zeppelin, "is to support the Indians in their claims of aboriginal rights. When these are restored, swindle them of their rights again."

CHAPTER SIX

Owls and Peeping Tomcats

The next Monday our seminar group seemed strangely depleted after the previous Friday's mob scene. I commented on this to Mr. Zeppelin.

"Yes, we're back to the hard core," he agreed. "It's a pity you were unable to persuade my colleagues to continue their participation in our endeavours."

"I tried but when I said that the next topic on the agenda was arts and letters they promptly lost interest."

"A pity, but understandable. After the excitement of our discussions about women anything else is going to be anticlimacteric. I don't know whether we learned anything much about the feminine and sports components of the Canadian identity but it was good fun. The men enjoyed themselves thoroughly and asked me to thank you again for your kind hospitality."

"A pleasure." I fiddled with my clipboard. "I seem strangely loath to start a new subject. As you say, anything else is going to be a letdown."

"Like kissing a pretty girl who has been eating sardines," suggested Mr. Zeppelin.

"Well, let's get started." I printed 'Arts & Letters' boldly across the top of the blank page in front of me and tapped my teeth with my pen.

"It seems to me," I began, "that in so far as the arts are concerned, Canada is in a bad way. This is unfortunate because the quality of the arts is valid criterion of the cultural development of a nation."

"The best criterion of the cultural level of a people is the quality of their toilets. A nation with smelly toilets is lacking in cultural worth."

"It's an interesting theory," I admitted, "but we can hardly apply to the Canada Council for a grant to travel around the world doing a quantitative sniffing of toilets to see how Canada compares with others."

"Why not? It makes more sense than some of the things they've supported."

"True. But on this basis Canada would probably come out fairly well on the sniffing scale. And France at the bottom. However, France is big in the bidet field which may compensate to some extent and introduce a variable in your hypothesis."

"Not really."

"You know, you have a point about plumbing," I admitted, after a few moments' thought. "The Minoans had running water in their biffies; think of the preoccupation of the Romans with their beautiful and sumptuous baths; picture the magnificent Arabian fountains and pools; the Greek temples; the Scandinavian saunas. Cleanliness may not be next to godliness but it does tell you something about a people. On the other hand, Versailles was built, as far as I know, without a john in the whole place. And look at what has happened to Venice."

"Crane is a greater benefactor to mankind than Rockefeller," said Mr. Zeppelin.

"An extrapolation of your effluvium theory would lead us to Canada's present preoccupation with deodorants," I suggested.

"It has been said that the soul is located in the armpit," stated Mr. Zeppelin.

"Before this leads you off on another theory of cultural evaluation, let us score Canada high on the sniffing scale, or should I say low, and push on to other matters."

"We have been using the term cultural rather loosely," I said thoughtfully. "I suppose we should ask ourselves what we mean by the culture of a race."

"Yes, let's do." Mr. Zeppelin pretended an enthusiasm I suspected was bogus.

"Okay. Let us define culture as a composite of the attributes of a sociological group."

"When we've got that we've got the Canadian identity."

"True. In Canada then, our culture embraces everything from chuckwagon races to symphony concerts; from-,"

"From manure spreaders to atom bombs," suggested Mr. Zeppelin.

"Which leads me to comment that with the high impact of science on our society today, some knowledge of science is essential to an appreciation of our culture. The least cultured but educated people today are English professors, steeped in Chaucer and Milton, with no knowledge of science, and arrogantly oblivious of their deficiencies. Culture is not synonymous with the arts." I banged my clipboard with my hand.

"Bravo. Spoken like a true scientist."

"However, it is true that an appreciation of the gentle arts is essential to a cultivated individual. It is in this area that I feel Canada is woefully deficient-art, drama, literature and so forth. I suppose Canada is not much worse off than the rest of the world. The whole modern world is a mess arts-wise, as the Americans say. Modern music is a cacophony; painting is nothing but dabs and dribbles; architecture offers egg crates piled on egg crates; sculpture is a meaningless jumble; writing is scatological nonsense; and drama is prurient tripe. The arts should contribute beauty not a message or a discord of sound or vision. The modern arts contribute cultural pollution."

"Wow," said Mr. Zeppelin slapping his hands together with a whack. "You've sure delivered a haymaker at the arts I must say. Press on, Professor, under a full head of sawdust!"

"What makes me mad," I continued, "is that many of these artists are very able but they deliberately produce junk. Their efforts are not, as you might suspect from the results, perverted in order to hide the fact that they have no ability. Picasso, believe it or not, could really paint. Lots of our Canadian composers are good musicians but they produce a strident dissonance; our writers are able but they distort their talents. There's a world-wide conspiracy of perversity. They don't produce things I like."

"Aha, there's the nub of the situation." Mr. Zeppelin pointed an accusatory finger at me. "If you'll pardon me for saying so, Professor, I think you're being narrow-minded and petulant. Because you don't like something doesn't mean it's no good."

"It does to me."

"Shame on you."

"What other criterion can I use? I really don't understand what these characters are trying to do."

"Aha, again. You condemn things because you don't understand them. That is an attitude unworthy of a scientist and a pedaglug. Do you understand Einstein's theory of whatever?"

"No."

"I submit I've proved my point."

"It's a long jump from Einstein's theory of relativity to a picture that can be hung upside down for all the difference it makes."

"Not really. You don't understand either of them but you accept one and not the other."

"You shouldn't have to go to an expert to interpret art. It should speak for itself."

"Maybe it is speaking for itself but you're not listening, or if you're listening you're not hearing. The message is going in one ear and out the other end."

"I have a strong suspicion there's no message there at all. At any rate, the language is not that of the common man, I can tell you. And it should be."

"Everyone to his own taste, said the old lady as she kissed the cow."

"Well, do you like or understand what's going on in modern arts?"

"Unfortunately not."

"Aha, right back at you," I shouted triumphantly.

"But that doesn't mean I reject it out of hand. If I rejected everything in life I didn't understand there wouldn't be much left. I figure a lot of these guys are trying new things, feeling their way, experimenting."

"If a scientist does an experiment which is a failure he pours it down the sink. If a painter tries an experiment which is a failure he puts a frame around it and sells it to the National Gallery; if a dramatist has a failure he sells it to the CBC."

"Who's to say it's a failure?"

"I am," I shouted.

Mr. Zeppelin shrugged and spread his hands. "We're back to that."

"I'd like to see Canadian artists lead the world in a movement back to sanity."

"I've heard say that art reflects life."

"I didn't think life was in that bad shape," I snapped.

"It is and our artists are saying so. I suppose you would like to go back to Robert Service, to the Group of Seven, and Mark Kenny."

Mr. Zeppelin sighed. "If you're an example, art appreciation is in a bad way in Canada."

"I'll be appreciative when there's something worth appreciating," I shouted.

Mr. Zeppelin shook his head sadly.

I didn't feel I was coming out too well in this exchange so I decided to try putting him on the defensive. "Do you like modern classical music?"

"Yes, some of it, very much. Some I don't understand."

"It passeth understanding."

Mr. Zeppelin looked disappointed in me. "I remember when I was a member of the Hungarian Woodwind Quintette," he began, "we-,"

"You were a member of the Hungarian Woodwind Quintette?" I asked in surprise. "What did you play?"

"First bassoon. We often played for royalty."

"Royalty in Hungary?"

"Yes. The King of the Gypsies. He liked our music so much he knighted me and gave me his secret formula for making wine out of Brussels sprouts."

I laughed, my equanimity restored. "I shall try to continue with less acerbity."

"Your emotion does you credit. More Canadians should get worked up about these matters. For example, the disgraceful lack of support which Canada provides for artists and writers."

"I agree completely. It is a tragedy that the only time a Canadian is appreciated in Canada is after he's hit it big in the States. The CBC is a farm team for the NBC. A typical Canadian loudly deplores the lack of support by Canadians for their artists, and then switches to the other channel."

"Television is a potent cultural force," said Mr. Zeppelin gravely.

"It is?" I exclaimed in surprise.

Mr. Zeppelin nodded. "Yes. I finished Hoot Gibson's *Decline and Fall of the Roman Empire* in one week just reading during commercials."

I laughed, feeling a little foolish. "You lead me so far up the garden path sometimes that I come back with daisies in my hair. However, I serve a useful function. A performer needs an appreciative audience. That's part of Canada's problem I guess. In the arts one needs three things - the writer, the performer, and the audience. I have maligned the first, the performers go elsewhere; and the audience is apathetic. There's a chicken and egg syndrome here I suspect."

"Another tripod," suggested Mr. Zeppelin with a wink.

"Yes, but let's not work it to death."

"We already have."

"Poof."

Mr. Zeppelin leaned forward and pointed his stein at me.

"Now, Professor, I am going to challenge you on some of your opinions. I have permitted, nay, I confess, encouraged you to go out on a limb and now I am going to saw it off. You have demonstrated a regrettably narrow and bourgeois attitude towards the arts."

I bridled but he shook his stein at me.

"We agreed initially that our culture embraced everything from manure spreaders on up, but you, with typical middle-class pretentiousness have zeroed in on the whipped cream. There's a whole pop culture quite apart from this which is jolly good. Our entertainers and popular musicians are top flight which is why they are in great demand elsewhere."

"They play too loudly," I complained.

He waved me aside. "But to return to the level where your affectation took us, Canada has some excellent symphony orchestras which are being appreciated and supported by the public and which are now performing some fine Canadian compositions. Furthermore, in belated recognition of public desires, governments have now built better facilities for concerts, opera, drama and so forth. I can remember, not so long ago, when visiting artists here had to perform in the 'Cowbarn' where the aroma of its previous occupants lingered noticeably."

"Yes, I remember," I smiled.

"Next, take the ballet, which you didn't even mention. Canada has some of the finest ballet companies in the world."

"I don't like ballet. All that jumping around in-,"

"Shame on you. Then let's look at Canadian drama which you have ridiculed. There are now a number of excellent professional and amateur theatrical groups across the country. We need more I know, but the quality of the performances I have seen often compares very favourably with those I have seen abroad. Also they are experimenting and producing the work of Canadian writers which is getting steadily better under this stimulus. I think you were wrong in being quite so derogatory of Canadian audiences although I am well aware that doctors' wives only go to show off their minks. But these theatres are attracting a growing clientele of knowledgeable and appreciative people."

"Well, I concede-,"

"You have maligned the CBC. Many of their programs are excellent. Furthermore, the CBC is doing its best to foster Canadian talent."

"Well, I-,"

"Next, writing. There is a growing number of fine novelists and, in particular, good historical writers. French-Canada has a delightful, unique literature all its own which is a justification for bilingualism even if nothing else is. Surprisingly enough, Canada is remarkably strong in the area of poetry. Have you read some of the recent Canadian poetry?"

"No, not much."

"Any?"

I fidgeted. "No," I confessed.

Mr. Zeppelin smote his forehead. "Oh, the tragedy of it all. This self-appointed authority has not even peeked into Galileo's microscope yet condemns what he does not see. How typically Canadian." He took a long draught of beer while I sat in sulky silence. He wiped the foam from his lips with his handkerchief.

"To come down to a more mundane level of cultural dissemination, I would make a brief reference to Canadian newspapers which I think are surprisingly good. I say surprisingly because they don't have much competition and don't have to be as good as they are. They publish a lot of garbage, and who should know better than I, but they convey the Canadian scene rather well. The editorial writers are almost uniformly competent, although I often disagree with their position."

"I agree completely on the newspaper bit," I interjected. "You only have to travel in the States for awhile to appreciate our Canadian newspapers. For one thing you practically never find any reference to Canada; international affairs get a cursory and biased once over lightly. They confine themselves primarily to murders, rapes and local political corruption, preferably combining all three."

"I'm glad you agree with me on something," grimaced Mr. Zeppelin. "How do you feel, Professor, about the rest of my diatribe?"

"I feel I've been well and truly shafted," I admitted ruefully. "And I suspect that I deserved some of it. I accept your reaming out with such good grace as I can muster. However, one area you didn't touch on is modern painting and sculpture. I hold fast to my original contention that it is dreadful."

Mr. Zeppelin blew out his lips. "I'm afraid I must agree," he conceded sadly. "The National Gallery looks like a kindergarten decorated by prankish children for a Hallowe'en party."

I chewed on my pen. "You have made a case that Canada is making progress in many of the arts but-,"

"But we should and could be doing much more," he interrupted.

"I wonder which form of art, if any, characterizes Canada particularly."

"What do you mean?"

"Well, in Italy it's opera; in Russia, ballet; France, the can-can; Spain, bullfights; England," I paused.

"Darts," suggested Mr. Zeppelin.

"I'll accept that. Now, how about Canada?"

"Gazing at our navels trying to find our identity."

"Try again."

"Curling?"

"It has been said that curling, like sex, is not a spectator sport."

"It is in the United States."

"Curling?"

"No, sex."

"Hmm. I see. So you think voyeurism is the national American sport? Maybe you're right. But is Canada any different?"

"Canadians are less honest. The American male is a lascivious owl; the Canadian male is a peeping tomcat."

"If the States can take credit for originating the striptease, what original art form has Canada contributed?" I asked.

Mr. Zeppelin chewed on his mustache. "The totem pole and the RCMP Musical Ride." He frowned. "I don't believe the States originated the striptease. Think of the Arabian Nights, dance of the seven veils, and all that."

"They've developed and refined it to its present nadir anyhow. The only thing the States has in common with ancient Greece is that they both require their goddesses to go around with their clothes off. But the Greek goddesses didn't take it off petal by petal while the satyrs shrieked eureka. Diana was a work of art, not a sex symbol."

"I think you are being highly selective in your mythology," complained Mr. Zeppelin. "However, there's really nothing lascivious about nakedness. Hence the tease. It's the old peek-a-boo that's intriguing. Voyeurism is visual vandalism."

I fidgeted with my clipboard. "Well, to return to the arts, if we follow our procedure of comparing ourselves with the United States, it's small consolation to be able to say that Canada is in better shape, culture-wise, than they are."

"Damning with faint huzzahs," grunted Mr. Zeppelin.

"Making fun of the Americans' cultural affectations is an old sport which I'm not particularly keen to get involved in, but I would be interested to see if Canadians are really any better. While the Washington Monument obviously didn't require much imagination to design, it's no worse than the Centre for the Performing Arts, or whatever they call it, in Ottawa, which looks like a rock quarry turned inside out. In the great middle classes, the ultimate in American cultural pretension is a swimming pool in the backyard; in Canada it's iron flamingos in the frontyard. At least we've had the sense not to disfigure our beautiful mountains with colossal caricatures. Presidents are not chosen for their beauty but why advertise the fact."

"We love their pictures on a piece of lettuce."

"That's where they should be left."

Mr. Zeppelin rubbed his nose thoughtfully. "One of the problems facing the Americans is that they have no cultural tradition that didn't start twenty minutes ago. Canada is in better shape because we have retained our association with Britain and feel we have inherited the best of it. Also we have the advantage of two founding cultures and, while we have no political ties with France, we embrace an extension of that rich tradition. American roots are in shallow soil. They pretend to despise what they do not have but, except for a seeking of a tradition, how can you account for London Bridge suffering a fate worse than falling down?"

"I think it's simply a manifestation of their magpie proclivities," I affirmed. "Americans collect anything and everything, junk as well as masterpieces. They're the biggest suckers in the world for geegaws-lead Eiffel Towers and plaster Taj Mahals. They also collect original Titians with equal enthusiasm. When they travel they want to take home with them any item they can lay their hands on, provided someone else wants it or values it. That's why they've bought up so many of the world's great masterpieces. I'm not at all sure they got them because they appreciate them. Canadians rise superior to the temptation by being unable to afford the luxury. This puts us in a splendid position to be critical of the Americans."

Mr. Zeppelin laughed. "Magpies with bank accounts. Wonderful. Well, they sure flit around the world cawing loudly."

"Magpies don't caw," I complained. "They go 'brack, brack'."

"Flap your wings, Professor."

"Poof." I felt a little foolish. "Yes, Americans travel about a great deal. Travel is supposed to be broadening since it exposes one to the culture of other nations. The Americans are the most widely travelled of any nation in the world yet are the most parochial. The problem is that Americans are more interested in travelling than in arriving. They flit from Hilton to Hilton with as little contact with the natives as possible and when they arrive they form the wagon train into a circle. An American doesn't really visit abroad. He carries with him his aura of Scranton or Chicago and peeks out of it at his surroundings. He doesn't like anything he sees because it's different from what he's used to. He compares, unfavourably and out loud, what he sees with what he has back home."

"Are Canadians any different?" asked Mr. Zeppelin.

"To determine that is the object of our exercise. Yes, I think so. We can't afford the Hilton rates, for one thing. We have less money so we are less resented. There are fewer of us so there is less clotting and Canadians never clot with Americans. Indeed, Canadians abroad avoid Americans like the plague, largely so we won't be mistaken for one. I really think Canadians do a better job of getting to meet and mingle with the people in other lands."

"You are being very harsh on our American colleagues," observed Mr. Zeppelin. "Americans who visit Canada don't behave like that."

"You're quite right. Americans feel completely at home in Canada so they are reasonably well mannered. It's when they travel abroad that they put their best foot forward and into their mouths."

Mr. Zeppelin rose to stretch his legs. He walked over to the cooler in the shade and returned with three bottles of beer, one of which he gave to Robespierre who was dozing in his favourite spot. He opened the other bottles and handed one to me. He stood staring thoughtfully down at me.

"Do you think there is a characteristic Canadian sense of humour? Or possibly I should ask first, do Canadians have a sense of humour at all?"

"Affirmative to both questions," I answered. "And it is a very important point you have raised relative to our considerations."

"It is? Well, bully for me." He returned to his chair.

"Yes. A nation's wit and humour are a most important aspect of its personality. You learn more about a country's character from its humourists than from its historians. What a country laughs at discloses its soul. Sick jokes reveal a sick society. A nation than can laugh at itself is self-confident; a nation that makes jokes in adversity will recover; a nation that loses its sense of humour is a menace."

Mr. Zeppelin nodded. "The cause of two world wars."

"Exactly. As was pointed out yesterday, a sense of humour enables you to see your own absurdity. If this is lost a sense of proportion is lost; if one takes oneself too seriously, judgement is warped and the soul is twisted."

"Possibly the same factors are involved in religious intolerances," suggested Mr. Zeppelin thoughtfully.

"Yes, fanaticism and humour are incompatible."

"Well, where does Canada rate on the laugh-meter? I am relieved, after what we have said, that you feel Canadians do have a sense of humour. You also implied that we have a type of humour which is typically Canadian. Is that right?"

"Yes, I think we do. It is less boisterous than the Latins; less witty than the British; less raucous than the American; and less subtle than the Oriental. But we do have a quiet, characteristic Canadian humour."

"What are its characteristics?"

I scratched my head. "It's hard to define. It has nuances of the other races I have mentioned but muted." I doodled on my clipboard. "Much humour has a basis in vulgarity."

"Is that a fact?" said Mr. Zeppelin with a very straight face.

"There is a frontier saltiness to Canadian humour which is highly creditable. A man who has no streak of commonness in him is no man at all."

"Ah," breathed Mr. Zeppelin. "Again I am relieved."

"Humour manifests itself in ways peculiar to its environment. I recall being out in the bush with a group of scientists one time when our Indian guide found a muskrat in a trap which a friend of his had set. Our guide skinned the muskrat and then put the carcass back in the trap. He went around all day with a smile on his face thinking of his friend's reaction when he found that trap. That's typical Canadian humour, but how would you explain it to an Englishman or a Swede? Indeed, would they even think it amusing?"

Mr. Zeppelin huffed appreciatively. "Well I do. Wonderful."

"One of the interesting variations in nations is their reactions to humour. The Latins convulse; the Americans guffaw; the English grimace faintly; and Canadians titter."

"Well, I'm no titterer," stated Mr. Zeppelin with an exaggerated chuckle.

"You titter with the bass stops, that's all."

"Poop. Do you have any more examples of typical Canadian humour, Professor?"

"No, not at my fingertips." I thought for a moment. "There is a story that's been around for awhile-I don't know where it came from-that would require a Canadian background to appreciate. The story goes like this. The scene is a western Canadian prairie on which two buffalo are grazing. Two cowboys ride by. One cowboy says to his partner, 'that's a scruffy looking pair of buffalo!' When they had ridden past, one buffalo turns to the other and says, 'I just heard a discouraging word'."

Mr. Zeppelin laughed in a restrained way. "Yes, an Englishman might have trouble with that one. As a matter of fact, so do I."

"Thank you, music lovers," I said. "Well, to endeavour to summarize our discussions on arts and letters, I take it that we are agreed that Canadians have a good sense of humour but have a way to go in so far as the arts are concerned."

"Agreed."

"Maybe the humour is the more important anyhow. A sense of humour is a divine gift that makes life tolerable."

"Amen," said Mr. Zeppelin.

CHAPTER SEVEN

Pangloss Downtown

"One area we haven't touched on yet which is certainly important in the Canadian identity is the field of business," I said to Mr. Zeppelin at our next session. "I wonder how we can get at it. Neither of us is a businessman and I'm afraid we don't know enough about the subject to do much with it."

"I know a guy in the seed and feed business if you want to get to the grass roots," offered Mr. Zeppelin.

"No, I don't think so, thanks. We need someone higher up in the field of finance."

"Talk to your banker."

"I don't even know my banker. The only communication I have with him is the occasional curt note saying that I'm overdrawn and will I please do something about it."

"Ask some of your pals in economics on campus."

"Hell, economics professors only know enough to win appointments to Royal Commissions and you know what they accomplish." Mr. Zeppelin nodded sadly. We sat and pondered the problem for several minutes.

"I know what I would like to do," I said. "I wish we could get into one of those cocktail parties for executives-you know the kind-where the comptroller picks up the tab. I understand that's where most of the wheeling and dealing in high finance takes place. But professors never get invited to those affairs. Hmm, I wonder." I let an idea coast around in my head.

"Maybe I could get Jerry Vernon to wangle us an invitation. He's a big wheel in the insurance racket and keeps me poor by selling me life insurance. He's an interesting character who just might be able and willing to swing it. I'll give him a jingle."

I went into the house to phone Jerry. I returned after a few minutes to report to Mr. Zeppelin, making the okay sign with my thumb and finger.

"We're in luck," I said enthusiastically. "One of the big investment firms is having a bash tonight to enable the business community to meet one of their moguls from New York. Just perfect. The screwy idea of taking a couple of professors to a business cocktail party appealed to Jerry's sense of humour. Incidentally, for tonight you're a visiting professor from abroad interested in Canadian finance. Okay?"

"Sure, why not."

"Jerry phoned Frank Jal, the local manager involved so it's all set and we won't be crashing the party. Excellent." I rubbed my hands together enthusiastically.

"Hmm. Frank Jal," mused Mr. Zeppelin. "He drinks an awful lot of martinis made with Fockink gin."

"Oh, do you know him?"

"No, but his house is on my route. Your garbageman knows more about you than your doctor and clergyman combined."

"Will he recognize you tonight?"

"No, nobody knows their garbageman."

"Except me."

"Yeah, you're a character."

"Thanks. Nicest thing that's been said to me today."

"I meant it kindly. Where's the party and what time?"

"It's in the Borneo Room of the Chateau Astor at eight o'clock. Shall I pick you up?"

"No, thanks. I'll meet you in the lobby at eight."

Thus it was that at eight o'clock that evening I met Mr. Zeppelin in the lobby of the hotel. I didn't see him until he lumbered up from a deep chair and came towards me. I had never seen him out of uniform before. He was impeccably dressed in a black broadcloth suit with a dark wine vest across which dangled a gold watch chain. His usually droopy mustache was waxed to neat perfection. But what really knocked me for a loop was a monocle screwed into one of his big baggy eyes. I stood open-mouthed in amazement.

"Good evening, Professor," he said courteously.

"Where the hell did you get that?" I blurted, pointing at the monocle.

"I always wore it to state functions in Hungary," he explained. "Would it be out of place tonight?"

"My god, yes."

"Very well," he said politely, dropping the monocle into a vest pocket.

"Whew." I breathed a sigh of relief. I lit a cigarette with shaking hands. Then I started having some second thoughts.

"No, just a minute. You're supposed to be a visiting professor from abroad, so why not? There's no way with your size you're going to be inconspicuous anyhow, so we might as well go all out. Sure, what the hell. You'll be a knockout."

"Whatever you say." Mr. Zeppelin fished the monocle out of his vest pocket and returned it to his eye.

I stood back and admired him. "You're beautiful," I enthused. Mr. Zeppelin grinned at me. "Let's go," I said, leading the way up to the mezzanine floor.

As we approached the Borneo Room we could hear a hum of voices and clinking of glasses. Jerry Vernon met us at the door. Jerry was thin, dark and jumpy with a long nose and a crooked, turned down mouth. He had a keen, sardonic wit and usually spoke in short sharp bursts.

"Jerry, this is Professor Zeppelin of the University of ah, ah-,"

"Zagreb," put in Mr. Zeppelin helpfully.

"Yes, Zagreb."

"Gad, you're well named," said Jerry looking at Mr. Zeppelin's ponderous size. "In thirty years in business here that's the first monocle I've come across. Delighted to meet you, Professor. Let us go in and meet the flotsam and jetsam of the Canadian business swamp. It's low tide. I gather, Professor, you have an interest in the machinations of the Canadian world of finance. You won't learn it from Merv, that's for sure."

"Yes," rumbled Mr. Zeppelin. "I felt it would be of interest to compare Canadian business procedures with those elsewhere."

"Well, you won't learn much here, but come along."

There was no receiving line at the door so we pushed our way into the crowded room, Jerry leading the way. Everyone was talking but nobody seemed to be listening. Glasses were in every hand. As we edged our way towards the bar, Mr. Zeppelin's imposing bearing and monocle drew considerable attention. There were many 'double-takes' and stares of amazement. As we moved along we left a trail of nudges and sudden silences.

When we reached the bar Jerry asked us what we would have. I ordered an Old Bushmills on the rocks and Mr. Zeppelin a cognac. While we waited for Jerry to get the drinks we examined the noisy crowd. I noticed that Mr. Zeppelin had adopted an imperial and grand manner which suited him admirably. The conversation around us had to do principally with football, golf scores and the financial difficulties of some group known as Consolidated something or other. When Jerry returned we toasted ourselves in silent gesture and sipped our drinks.

"Well, where do you want to start, my professorial pundits?" asked Jerry. "You see before you the elite of the city's business snakepit. That's what you wanted and there they are in all their bibulous beauty." He waved his glass in a sweeping gesture. "What do you think of them, Professor Zeppelin?"

"Very interesting," said Mr. Zeppelin solemnly.

"What's this talk about Consolidated something?" I asked. "I've picked up some snatches of conversation about it."

"Rumour has it," explained Jerry, "that the reason Philby is here from head office is to look into a loan made by Frank Jal, our ulcer-ridden host, to Consolidated Holdings. Frank may find himself assigned to a cushy berth in Gopher Hollow, Saskatchewan, when the smoke has cleared away."

"Very interesting," said Mr. Zeppelin adjusting his monocle to study the room. "But why do all these people come here? What is the purpose of this gathering?"

"What do you think, Merv?" asked Jerry, turning to me.

"Well, it's a party, so I suppose they just come to enjoy themselves at someone else's expense," I suggested.

"That's where you're wrong. Nobody is enjoying himself. Let me demonstrate." He reached out and poked a lugubrious individual who was glowering into his drink. "Hi, Arthur, enjoying yourself?"

Arthur looked startled. "Are you kidding? I hate these things and my feet are killing me. I hear Philby's in town to cut Frank's throat. Serves him right for putting a bundle on Consolidated. He sure got his you-know-what in a ringer on that one."

"Yeah, I hear the same," said Jerry. Arthur sadly inched his way toward the bar. Jerry turned back to us. "See, Professor? No one is enjoying himself. Try again."

"Do they come to talk business?" asked Mr. Zeppelin.

"Not in the sense that you mean it. No one undertakes to do any business here. In fact it would be a solecism to try. However, it is a business gossip exchange and therefore very useful. One has to know the state of linen in the next street."

"I suppose they're promoting business, indirectly," I hazarded.

"Yes, they are promoting themselves on the well-established premise that goods and services will follow. Business is done between those with the same pretensions. The important thing is to be here. They would be terrified not to be. They come to strengthen their egos by sharing contempt for those who are not here."

"Sort of a mutual admiration society," I suggested.

"No, actually they hate each other. They come to be renewed in their identity and reassured of their own importance by association with a group of their peers who have the same set of values. Also they must renew their belief in the importance of what they are doing. They think they have the best of all possible worlds, evidence of ulcers, coronaries and psychoses notwithstanding, and come to associate with other Panglosses. Furthermore, they are basically seeking a reaffirmation of reality. 'I drink, therefore I am'."

"And here I thought it was just a party," I exclaimed.

Jerry looked at me disdainfully. He turned to Mr. Zeppelin. "That's the way it is in Canada, Professor. Is it any different where you come from?"

Mr. Zeppelin studied the matter carefully. "There seems to be a peculiarly Canadian intensity to the situation as you have described it not seen elsewhere, but I would say the set of values is essentially the same from Tokyo to New York, or from Zagreb to Toronto."

"I thought as much," said Jerry. "Now that you have the overall picture would you like me to explain the function of the various categories represented here?"

"That would be most helpful," said Mr. Zeppelin.

"Okay, first, accountants. They're the score keepers of the

money game. An accountant is a bookkeeper with a superiority complex. An auditor is a bookkeeper who adds up columns of figures that other bookkeepers have added up to see if he gets the same answer. He always does. This is known as 'professional courtesy'."

"Do they qualify as financiers?" I asked.

"Certainly not. A financier is a businessman who owes so much money that the bank can't afford to let him go broke. Therefore the more money you owe the wealthier you are. Anderson of Consolidated Holdings will know tomorrow if he is a financier or a bum. The margin is often very narrow."

"What is your category in this set-up?" I asked.

"I'm an investment consultant, a legalized bookie dealing in stocks."

"I thought you were an insurance salesman."

"Please." Jerry held up his hand with a pained expression. "Salesmen sell things. The people here hire salesmen. I do write a little insurance as a service to friends."

"I suppose there are some lawyers around," I enquired. Mr. Zeppelin snorted.

"Yes, most of the jokers here will hardly go to the john without consulting a lawyer. Lawyers become operative when moral laws break down. They're needed here, believe me."

"Are clergymen ever invited to these affairs?," asked Mr. Zeppelin.

"Oh yes," answered Jerry. "Always. One or two. They're invited to lend respectability to the rite. You can't have money changers in the temple but it's okay to have priests in the money-mart. They make out all right from these affairs. A good touch is better than bingo any day. The businessmen figure they're making a down payment on salvation. It's cheap because it comes out of income taxes."

"How about doctors?"

"Yes, there's always a clot of doctors around."

"Why?"

"Several reasons. First, they have the most money and the least business sense of any group in the community. Pigeons all. Second, for some obscure reason they are thought to lend prestige. Probably goes back to the days of tribal witchcraft when the medicine man was thought to have special powers. The modern shamans foster this illusion and manage to maintain some aplomb even when giving a prostatic massage." Jerry stretched his neck, searching through the mob.

"Doctors tend to coagulate at these things. Yes, there they are, over by the window. The one facing us wearing a vandyke is an obstetrician. They used to be mid-wives, now they're mostly mid-husbands."

"Down boy," I laughed.

Jerry grinned his lopsided grin. "Enough of my charitable analyses," he said. "Come over and meet our cheerful host. We can locate him by the aroma of Fockink gin martinis." Mr. Zeppelin and I exchanged knowing looks.

Jerry pulled us through the mob up to a short, waterlogged individual with the falsely jovial manner of an early morning radio announcer. His eyes, which were bulbous and watery, seemed to float in his head. I felt if he blew his nose too hard his eyes would squirt.

"Hi, Jerry," he greeted us. "How's the fastest tongue in the West? I sure admired the way you put it over on the Japhic boys on that land deal out at the airport. Pretty smooth. This Jerry," he said to me, "talks like he didn't have any more sense than a university professor but he's smart like soap in the eyes." He nudged me knowingly with his elbow, sloshing my drink down my shirt. He made vague sponging motions, dropping his cigar ashes in my glass. Jerry performed the introductions.

"Sorry about that crack about professors," said Frank. "I'd forgotten Jerry was going to bring you two gentlemen along. No harm intended. Bad timing I must say." He turned to Mr. Zeppelin.

"Well, Professor Zeppelin, it is a great pleasure and an honour to have a man of your stature-figuratively and literally, I see-join our sorry soiree."

"It is my esteemed pleasure," said Mr. Zeppelin politely.

"Your reputation has preceded you, sir," continued Frank unctuously. "I'm delighted you have found the time in your no doubt crowded rounds to accept our humble hospitality. I am not unfamiliar with international finance myself and have often heard of you but never dreamed I would have the privilege of meeting you. I have read some of your writings with great interest."

"You are too kind," rumbled Mr. Zeppelin modestly.

"Come with me, sir. I would like you to meet one of my principals from New York, Mr. Philby. Is it Count Zeppelin?"

"Please, no titles," said Mr. Zeppelin with elaborate graciousness and a lordly wave of the hand.

"As you wish, sir," said Frank. "I understand and appreciate your modesty and reticence. Mr. Philby will be delighted to have the opportunity to meet you and to discuss international finance.

What do you think will be the impact of the EEC on the Canadian financial structure?"

"I feel there are definite pros and cons to be considered," said Mr. Zeppelin judiciously.

"You are absolutely right," agreed Frank, turning his back on Jerry and me to lead Mr. Zeppelin away through the mob.

Jerry grinned at me derisively. "You'd better grow a few feet and wear a monocle," he said. "Give me your glass and I'll get you a drink. Old Bushmills?"

"Right. And thanks." Jerry went off to the bar leaving me alone. I felt as out of place as a poker chip in a collection plate. I pulled my cuffs and projected my sophisticated look, a look which was meant to suggest that I knew everyone there but was looking specifically for an important contact who would approach at any moment. My manner was one of bored eclat, touched with arrogance, but ameliorated by charm. It didn't come off worth a damn; I was ignored completely.

At this point I was gratified to see someone I knew, Archie Thorpe. It gave me a sense of belonging.

"Hello, Archie," I said, pulling his coat sleeve.

"Uh, hi, Fred," said Archie, shaking my hand loosely and looking over my head.

"Merv," I said firmly.

"Uh? Oh, sure, Merv, of course. How are ya?"

I have known Archie around town for years. Whenever I met him at social affairs I always felt a bit like I used to many years ago when I danced with Bessie Bell at highschool affairs. She was a good foot taller than I was which made romantic rapport rather difficult to begin with. Bessie would dance with me but over my head she had her radar working for more eligible partners. Archie used the same approach. He would talk to me only long enough to identify over my head the most important (wealthy) person in the room and then he buzzed off. This device is used by many Canadian business and social ballet dancers. I am a good point of departure. For one thing, I am short so I don't obstruct the view; for another they've got nowhere to go but up.

Archie's antennae were working. He fixed his eye across the room and said, "Oh, there's Jules Forwick. Nice talking to you, Fred." And he moved off in the direction of a dollar sign in a pinstripe suit. I was alone again.

I was glad to see Jerry approaching through the crowd with my drink. As he handed it to me he asked, "What have you been doing to amuse yourself in my absence?"

"I had a chat, sort of, with Archie Thorpe."

"That Archie. If he had pruritus ani he'd be itchy all over." He held up his glass. "Here's to us, good people are seldom." We sipped our drinks.

"Your friend is a smashing success," continued Jerry. "Philby is very impressed and is taking him around to meet the native chiefs. Who is he?"

"A visiting professor. He's apparently well-known in international monetary affairs. You heard what Frank Jal said."

"Yeah. Frank is a climber, comes from an old alpine stock."

"Heh, heh."

"Well, shall we continue our study of the local fauna?"

"Sure, by all means. I enjoy your dirty thumbnail sketches."

"Where shall I pick it up?"

"As a beginning, who's the character over there with the hearing aid and his mouth open?"

"That's George Peevey. He's in advertising. It is the function of advertisers to induce people to buy things they don't want and can't afford. This is very useful since it enables those who make these things to buy things they don't want and can't afford. Buying is the backbone of our economy and advertisers are right there, zap, at the bottom of that backbone." Jerry made a sharp downward gesture with his forefinger.

"Is there anyone here from the creative world-music, literature, drama and so forth?"

"Certainly not. That would just confuse things. Anyone with a different set of values would be a threat to their own simple criterion of worth, namely money. The closest we get to the literary-minded are newspaper men. They can be identified by orange juice drinks, hyperemic noses and sunburned eyeballs."

"Why are professors never invited to these things?"

"Why should they? They have no money; they can't do anything for, or to, anybody here; they're not far enough up on the totem pole to lend prestige; and they aren't kooky enough, with rare exceptions, to lend colour. They're from dullsville, Daddy-o. What have you done recently that you're proud of?"

"Well," I replied huffily, "my last paper on the kidney function of the octopus caused-,"

"Octopus, schmoctopus."

I decided it best to change the subject. "Tell me, who is Philby and what exactly is he doing here?"

"He's a vice-president in the New York office in charge of colonies, which includes Canada, sort of a colonial secretary in the old sense. His job is to see that the Canadian economy functions to the advantage of the United States. He and his ilk have been very successful at it."

"How does it work?"

"Frank Jal's outfit is a typical case. They were a Canadian company which was bought up by Philby's group."

"I suppose this sort of thing is desirable because it brings in American money."

Jerry snorted. "American takeovers bring very little money into Canada. They use Canadian money to buy out Canadians."

"How?"

"By getting loans from Canadian banks. Banks are not patriotic institutions; they are in business to make money and if selling Canada makes them money that's all they care about."

"Why don't the banks lend the money to Canadians?"

"They figure American firms are a safer bet. Also it must be admitted that Canadian businessmen haven't shown the initiative and faith in their country which they should. They'd rather make a quick buck and get out. Mr. Beaver isn't eager anymore; he's alive and well and living in Palm Springs. Anyhow it would be easier for a Canadian to get a bank loan to open a firecracker factory in Taiwan than a brick factory in Thunder Bay."

"What do you think about all the American talk about continental planning?"

"Sure, they're saying let's pool our resources. It's my observation that any time somebody says to you 'let's pool our resources' then you've got more to put in the pot than he has. We have no obligation to maintain their standard of living as the highest in the world. I'm tired of being number two or three. I say hold on to our assets, make them pay through the teeth for any excess we don't need and let Canada be number one."

As Jerry downed his drink with determination, I looked across the room where Philby and Mr. Zeppelin were chatting animatedly with a group of people. Philby was a tall man with a charming boyish grin in a hard, pinched face.

"Mr. Philby doesn't appear to have horns," I commented.

"No, of course not. Hatchet men are chosen for their affability. He's been up here often enough to know how to avoid Canadian sensitivities. He can be charming and delightful but count your fingers after you've shaken hands with him. The Canadians who see the other side of the corporation are those in the head office in Toronto where they rotate a series of Madison Avenue cum Harvard hotshots as managers on an indoctrination apprenticeship in bloodletting. Jal, and others, stay out of it if they can and tranquilize their consciences with martinis. Jal's problem at the moment is that he lent money to C.H., a Canadian company, without the hook that would have tied them to Philby's chariot. My guess is that Philby will lend enough more money to C.H. to give him control. He'll borrow, from a Canadian bank, the money which Anderson of C.H. wouldn't be able to get."

"It sounds sad."

"It is. Things are starting to break up," he commented.

I became aware of a general shuffling towards the door. Mr. Zeppelin worked his way over to us. His baggy eyes, with the monocle still screwed securely in place, were sparkling.

"I have been invited," he announced in a pleased tone, "to join Mr. Philby out at Mr. Jal's home for a nightcap. It was very gracious and I couldn't very well refuse."

"The party after the party," laughed Jerry. "A noble Canadian institution with a long history of disasters, debacles and catastrophes."

"Sure, go ahead by all means," I said to Mr. Zeppelin. "But remember the pumpkin."

He looked pained. "Will I see you tomorrow, Professor?" he asked loftily.

"Yes, if you wish. The usual time, in my back, er, office. Will you be able to make it?"

"I shall keep the time open," he assured me graciously. He thanked Jerry for his hospitality with a stiff bow, and I'll swear I heard his heels click. With a flash of his monocle he was gone.

CHAPTER EIGHT

Bo Peep and Catherine the Great

The next morning Mr. Zeppelin arrived late. He climbed slowly down from the cab and made his way carefully to the gate, leaning heavily on Robespierre's shoulder.

When he got to the gate he bleated to me in a quavering voice, "call a minister, call a rabbi, call a doctor, call an undertaker. I am about to expire." He tottered into the yard with a worried Robespierre fussing along behind him.

"Mr. Zeppelin's very sick," said Robespierre. "He's got malaria and tropical scrud, he says."

"Ah, Robespierre, my faithful retainer," said Mr. Zeppelin in lugubrious tones. "I bequeath to you my collection of Guy Lombardo records and my gold ukelele pick. When I am gone you will find the latter in the bottom of the baking powder tin in the kitchen cupboard. Use it happily on festive occasions and think kindly once in a while of your dear departed friend." He extended one hand in a groping gesture.

"Now guide these faltering steps, once so full of bounce and the joy of life, to some sanctuary where I may die in peace and quiet."

He shuffled to his chair and, with Robespierre's help, lowered himself cautiously into it. He was not looking his best to say the least. His eyes were bloodshot and his skin had a greenish tinge.

"Ah, Professor." He turned his woebegone eyes upon me. "I am not long for this world. Would you act as witness for my last will and testicles?"

"No one ever died of a hangover," I stated brutally.

"I am making medical history," he groaned, rolling his eyes pathetically.

"To write a will you will need a lawyer," I said viciously. A spark returned to his eye but it soon faded. He put a shaky hand to his forehead.

"How can you be so savage to a man in such pitiable condition? Have you no heart, no mercy, no compassion, no beer?"

"Now stop playing King Lear," I said briskly. "A very touching performance but let's get down to business."

"Please." He leaned forward with his head in both hands. "The first trash can I tried to lift this morning, my head fell off and rolled down the alley like a football. Robespierre had to fetch it back." He straightened up slowly. He stuck out a furry tongue.

"Bleah. I think a parrot has been nesting in my mouth." He turned to Robespierre who had been hovering about, a look of dismay on his usually cheerful face.

"Doctor, would you please be so kind as to hand me a bottle of plasma, please." He pointed to the beer. Robespierre brought the beer which Mr. Zeppelin poured into a stein with a shaking hand.

"Listen to the row those bubbles are making," he complained. He drained the beer down, lay back in his chair with a great sigh and closed his eyes. His stomach emitted a loud gurgle.

"Hear that?" he cried. "My big guts are eating my little guts." He moaned loudly. "You have done what you can, Doctor," he said sadly to Robespierre. "The post mortem will undoubtedly prove you correct. You may withdraw." Robespierre took a bottle of beer to his usual place where he continued to watch Mr. Zeppelin with deep concern.

"I'm beginning to think I'll live," said Mr. Zeppelin, a little more cheerfully. He helped himself to another beer which he again polished off. A little colour returned to his face. "Oh, how I suffer in the interests of science."

"If it's any consolation, you were a smashing success last night. I congratulate you."

"Thank you. I guess I was at that."

"What is your impression of the business component of the Canadian identity?"

"It's in able but shaky hands this morning." He burped gently and rubbed his stomach. "I'm feeling much better. I guess this decaying carcass will last another day."

"What happened out at Jal's?"

"Some of it is fairly vague. Mr. Jal retired fairly promptly."

"You mean he passed out?"

"That's one way of expressing it. All in all it was quite a party." He passed a hand over his eyes. "A learned member of the bar fell downstairs, heh, heh; two guests had to be forcibly restrained from settling an argument with fisticuffs; and a distinguished surgeon went to sleep in the bathtub, which fortunately was empty at the time. I missed some of the fun because I was closeted with Philby and Anderson of Consolidated Holdings in discussions over that loan. I was brought in as consultant or adviser or something. I functioned by saying little, looking wise and being equivocal. Under my brilliant leadership, Philby has agreed to double the loan on the basis, I gather, that if he doesn't he'll lose the first half because Consolidated Holdings will go belly-up. Sound financial procedures, I presume. Both Philby and Anderson thanked me for my skillful arbitration when it was all over. I declined a seat on the board of directors of Consolidated Holdings, pleading international commitments. I gave the same answer to a Mr. Japhic who made overtures to me about joining his board in an advisory capacity."

"I think you were wise."

"I have no intention of getting my finger in any of those woodpecker nests, believe me. The business rat race is for wolves." He held his fingers to his eyes. "I think my skull has shrunk. Are my brains squirting out my ears?"

"Not yet. How long did the party go on?"

"I'm not sure. We had a grand singalong around the piano with some very good four part harmony-at least it seemed so at the time. I sang a solo entitled *She Was Grand to the Regiment but She was Rotten to the Corps*, which brought a tear to every eye. Anderson found one of Mrs. Jal's wigs-she was mercifully absent

I might add-which he donned for a stirring, if somewhat vulgar rendition of *It's Fine on the Rhine with a Fraulein full of Wine*. Somebody tried to juggle four billiard balls and wrecked the crystal chandelier. But what led me astray was a rousing game of 'Colonel Puff Puff'. I may say, however, that I did not disgrace myself, nor you, Professor. The honour of the University of Zagreb is intact."

"I had no concerns on that score," I assured him.

"Thank you."

"Well, now that we've had a taste of Canadian business life-or should I say sip-I would suggest that we turn our attention to economics."

"Wow, I'm sure in great shape for a topic like that. I'd better have another beer." He helped himself. While he poured the beer he continued speaking. "It would appear that economics has very little to do with business as far as I can see. Or the reverse."

"They must be interrelated in some way," I said vaguely. "I think it may be fairly said that the Canadian economy is in something of a mess."

"It's in worse shape than I am, which is really saying something." Mr. Zeppelin held the cold stein to his forehead.

"The Canadian economy is based on free enterprise," I said, feeling my way. "A free enterprise system is both simple and complex. The simple part is to make a profit; the complex part is how to do it. I have a vague feeling that my statement is not very profound."

Mr. Zeppelin closed his eyes. "In a free enterprise democracy, everyone has an equal right to diddle everyone else. But people differ in the size of their diddlers-no vulgarity intended."

"Very good," I nodded. "And the biggest diddler of all is the government. We always seem to end up back at the bloody government."

"That's for sure," agreed Mr. Zeppelin vehemently. "They've always got their hand in the working man's pocket. The Lord giveth and the government taketh away. Hallelujah."

"Look," I objected. "I'm tired of this 'working man' jazz. I pay taxes too, you know."

"Do you like it?"

"No, I don't. Do you think anybody in Canada believes the level of taxes is just, or fair, or necessary?"

"In two words, no."

"Then why don't they do something about it?"

"What can they do? None of the political parties offer any alternatives. All we get is a different hand in our pocket. Maybe we should start a new party with a platform to do away with money."

"You can't do away with money. You need capital to finance, ah, things," I said wisely.

"Yes, but money shouldn't earn any profit. It does no work. You ever see a dollar bill with sweat on its forehead?"

"That's contrary to basic economics. The people with money won't put it up if it doesn't earn more money," I objected.

"Get it from the government and make jobs for the unemployed."

"But the government gets its money from the people."

"They should get it from the people who have it, the wealthy guys."

"You mean tax the wealthy out of existence?"

"Sure, why not? Why should some fat slob be sitting on a pile of dough? Everyone should have the same income if they're working."

"You'd lose the profit motive. It's been tried and it doesn't work."

"The government should make everyone work, including the plutocraps who don't work now."

"You contradict yourself," I complained.

"Of course. That's a basic law of economics."

"I suspect that we don't know much about economics, like most Canadians."

"We don't need to know much for our purposes. Which is just as well. We're not trying to solve the economic ills of the country, just establish the Canadian identity. The Canadian ignorance is as much a part of our identity as our knowledge."

"Well said. You relieve my mind. Do you think we're average Canadians in this respect?"

"Yeah, between us we're about average."

"I get that," I stated stiffly. "One below and one above, eh?"
Mr. Zeppelin grinned. He was obviously beginning to recover his health. I decided not to pursue the subject. After all he was still not a well man. I changed the topic. "Now take the farmers-,"

"Everyone takes the farmers," said Mr. Zeppelin.

"No, they don't. The farmers are the coddled group in our society. If a farmer goes broke, the government bails him out; if a shoe store goes broke, too bad, Joe."

"The farmer is a working man and has to be protected from the money barons. But the farmers are feeling their oats. When they get unionized, then watch out."

"I can't afford steak now."

"Neither can the farmer."

"I gather you're a socialist," I said with a sneer.

"You're damn tooting. That's the only way to get a fair shake for the working man."

"You've swallowed a swindle. It's a political gimmick to get votes. The socialist party pretends it will take from the rich and give to the poor. This is known as Robin Hood-winking the public."

"Nonsense. It's up to the state to look after its citizens, all of them, particularly the indignants who can't take care of themselves."

"Or won't," I said. "Originally socialism tried to impose on society a tyranny of the incompetent; now it is trying to impose a tyranny of the slothful. With the attractions of welfare, unemployment insurance and guaranteed annual income they are fostering laziness and inertia. If a guy can make more money not working than working then who is going to work? If we use statistics the way Canada Manpower does then eventually nobody will be working and you have the welfare nirvana. The universities, with typical farsightedness, are already offering courses in how to use your leisure. It may be that Ass-sitting 37 will become the most practical course in the curriculum."

Mr. Zeppelin shook his head vigorously. "We are trying to get out from under the present tyranny of the vested money oligarchy. What we are saying is that every Canadian is entitled to a good standard of living and it's up to the state to see that he gets it. Furthermore, the citizens are the state so it's their own money."

"Well, I don't see why the state should provide something for people who can afford it themselves, like Medicare."

"I agree with you."

"You do? Then there must be something wrong in what I said. I'd better have another look at it."

"Pfui," said Mr. Zeppelin inelegantly. "You're a typical entrenched reactionary. As long as there are gross inequalities in income and as long as money keeps making money for the bums who are sitting on it, then let the wealthy pay and through the nose. And tax the hell out of them until they're getting only what they're worth to the state-not what a privileged position enables them to extort from their fellow citizens. Pfui again. Oh, my head. I shouldn't allow myself to get so worked up." He pressed his hands to his forehead.

"I'd better have another beer." He fetched bottles for all three of us.

"Another thing," Mr. Zeppelin continued, "consider the old age pensions. A bloody disgrace, that's what it is."

"I agree."

"You do? Then it's my turn to reappraise the situation. Politically you and I are about as far apart as Bo Peep and Catherine the Great."

"I have no political position," I stated. "I am a pragmatic realist."

"Poop."

"Anyhow, today I am trying to deal with economics, not politics," I continued.

"The smell of politics is all persuasive."

"Pervasive."

"That too."

I bit my pen in exasperation. "I'm finding my patience severely taxed today. It's a good thing-,"

"My god," shouted Mr. Zeppelin. "Are they taxing that now too? It was the only thing left." He held up his hands in horror.

"An unfortunate choice of words," I gritted. "I guess I have taxes on my mind." I hastily held up my hand. "Now leave that one lie, please."

Mr. Zeppelin pulled at his mustache. "With reference to an earlier comment, if you don't like paying taxes, then why do you do it?"

"A silly question. If I didn't, I'd go to jail."

"After considerable thought," said Mr. Zeppelin slowly, "I'd say that's a valid reason. However, although you or I would go to jail, the big-moneyed boys wouldn't."

"I suppose they'd pay a fine. If caught."

"The 'if caught' is the key phrase there. The big-moneyed boy would buy a smart lawyer-I'll rinse my mouth out later-and he'd find a loophole so our friend, the big-shot, would get off. The tax laws are designed by lawyers to be so confusing that only other lawyers can interpret them, which ensures continuing employment for guess who. An average guy can't afford one of these legal beagles so he goes to the pokey." He threw up his hands. "God help the poor working man. And professors." He added the last as an afterthought.

"The lawyers just put into jargon the principles of an economic plan laid down by the government." I thought that over. "Do you think, by the way, that the government does have an economic plan at all?"

"The government must have an economic plan," he asserted. "They couldn't have got things in such a bloody mess by accident."

"You're not suggesting that they made the mess on purpose, are you?"

"No. They accomplished it by sheer, unadulterated, blithering incompetence. It's quite a trick to combine spiralling inflation with rising unemployment, but they've done it."

"You can thank the unions for that."

Mr. Zeppelin sat bolt upright. "What the hell are you talking about?" he demanded. "The unions are the only stabilizing factor in our economy."

"Nonsense," I retorted. "The unions demand higher and higher wages all the time. The things they produce therefore cost more and more. That's inflation."

"Nonsense yourself," Mr. Zeppelin replied hotly. "The greedy financiers demand more income from their investments and put the prices up. The working stiff has to have higher wages to pay the inflated prices demanded by the manufacturers. And that's just to hold their own, let alone rectify some of the shamefully low salaries being paid to many of them."

"I'll grant you that at one time unions served a useful purpose," I conceded, "but -,"

"The job's only half done."

"But," I continued firmly, "nowadays they've gone too far. They are irresponsible, destructive and are victimizing the public."

"On the contrary. The unions represent the public interest. They see to it that the public is not victimized by the unscrupulous and irresponsible viciousness of the money grabbers. The unions insist that the workers, who are the public after all, get at least some share of the results of the sweat of their labour."

"The unions are putting people out of work by their excessive salary demands. The employers cannot afford to pay the same number of people these inflated wages. Therefore they must lay off workers. Those working are getting more money but there are fewer and fewer working. Those who aren't working go on welfare, at the expense of those who are working. If this continues, fewer and fewer workers will be supporting most of the population. Taxes will be so high that it won't be worthwhile to work. So then where are you?"

"Stuff and nonsense. The unions are pressuring for more jobs for more people but are insisting that the workers get a decent living wage and are not exploited by the financiers. Why should the workers work their guts out to make more money for somebody who has lots to begin with? Why should they?" Mr. Zeppelin was red in the face and glowering at me.

"The unions demand so much of the pie that there's not enough left to justify a person hazarding his hard-earned money-,"

"Hard-earned. Hah!"

"-to employ people who are going to put him out of business."

"If a guy can't make money and still pay a decent wage then he shouldn't be in business. He must not be allowed to make money by exploiting the working classes." He pounded his leg with his fist.

"The unions have priced Canadian goods right out of the international market and-,"

"Just because the plutocrapers in other countries don't pay a decent wage is no reason why Canadian businessmen should be allowed to pay coolie wages too."

"Damn it, you've given me every Marxist cliché in the book," I said in exasperation.

"Well, you've given me every moth-eaten, rotten, capitalistic cliché in the book," Mr. Zeppelin snapped back.

"My clichés are better than your clichés," I replied angrily.

"Now, there's the remark of the week," said Mr. Zeppelin, laughing nastily.

"The unions have saddled Canadian business with an impossible burden by their absurd wage demands, decreased production, featherbedding and so on. They've fought every technological advance which-,"

"They have not. They've encouraged technological developments. But it's the duty of the unions to see that machinery is man's servant, not his master. The machines must create jobs, not put men out of work. And furthermore-,"

"And take strikes," I interrupted loudly. "Strikes cost the Canadian economy millions of dollars a year."

"Strikes are legal, they-,"

"They won't be for long if unions continue to abuse the privilege with wasteful, irresponsible and violent strike action. Strikes are an inefficient and wasteful means-,"

"They're not inefficient because they accomplish their objective, a fair deal for the working man. I would point out to you that strikes are legal and are the only weapon the victimized worker has. It is the only power he has to make the money-mad moguls give him-,"

"Society cannot permit itself to be blackmailed by a selfish, irresponsible minority group." I rose from my chair and pointed an accusing finger at him. "It's people like you who are promoting violent and destructive union tactics which are undermining our whole Canadian business structure and our democratic way of-,"

"Now just a god-damned minute," shouted Mr. Zeppelin, lurching out of his chair and jabbing me in the chest with a finger. "It's idiots like you who are trying to grind down the working man to make more money for the bankers. The unions are the bulwark of our Canadian way of life!"

"Like hell they are," I shouted, poking my finger in his chest. "The unions are a vicious unprincipled force unworthy of-,"

"You reactionary, fuzzy-headed apologist for the grasping exploiters of the working man!" roared Mr. Zeppelin.

"You, you-," I searched my mind for the ultimate insult. "You lawyer, you!" I cried.

Mr. Zeppelin let out a cry of pain and rage. He raised a ham-like fist.

Suddenly something precipitated itself between us. I fell back in surprise. So did Mr. Zeppelin. We stared in amazement. Robespierre stood between us brandishing a large shovel.

"You two shut up. Sit down and behave!" he shouted hoarsely. He shook the shovel at us again.

Mr. Zeppelin looked aghast. Then he laughed. "It looks as if arbitration has arrived," he said.

I finally gathered my wits together. "And by the size of that shovel I would say it's compulsory arbitration." I sat down feeling foolish.

Mr. Zeppelin threw himself into his chair laughing uproariously. "Well, Professor, I guess we've fairly well demonstrated the dichotocacophony in Canadian labour-management relations. Huff, huff, huff."

CHAPTER NINE

The Mud of Parnassus

The next morning Mr. Zeppelin had recovered his health and good temper. We were both reluctant to make reference to the previous day's unfortunate contretemps. Robespierre was his usual cheerful self. We dawdled over the introductory beer ritual with amiable banter before settling down to our deliberations.

I finally picked up my pen to make some notations on my clipboard.

"One component of the Canadian identity we haven't discussed yet," I began, "is the university. Since the educational level of a nation is an important factor in its characteristics, it behoves us to give careful attention to this matter."

"Well, you should be in a position, Professor, to speak with authority on that topic," said Mr. Zeppelin. "It's your particular ball of wax."

"One would suppose so, of course," I conceded, "but maybe I'm too close to the university to see it in perspective. Trees and forest and all that. I would like to bring a fresh slant by viewing it through your eyes."

"Sure thing, Professor, I shall be happy to oblige. I can be your dissecting microscope of the Grave Academe and-,"

"That's Grove," I objected.

"I'm not so sure I wasn't correct. We shall see. Anyhow I shall be happy to goad you into a statement of your biases and then destroy them," he grinned happily.

"A person's biases are very precious to him, particularly if he doesn't think he has any. I suppose it is just barely possible I may have a few myself."

"Yeah, it's just possible," nodded Mr. Zeppelin, giving me a droll look. "However, each person figures he has soundly based conclusions. It's other people who have biases."

"Okay, you can put me on the defensive if you like. It will help me organize my thoughts and test my, er, soundly based conclusions."

"Agreed."

I sat in thought for a few minutes. "I have an idea," I said. "Our venture out the other evening into the world of business was such a success, why don't we try the format again? The university is putting on a reception tonight for a visiting fireman, Dr. Streiblatt, a Nobel Prize winner, who is visiting the campus for a few days. Why don't we go? Would you be willing?"

"I don't know." Mr. Zeppelin hesitated. "If they're going to be discussing some high-falutin' stuff then I'd be as out of place as a hiccup at a Baptist convention."

"No problem. It's a cocktail party. Anyhow, professors never discuss anything of any importance outside of their laboratories, and rarely there. I wouldn't suggest it if I thought you might be embarrassed. I am sure you would enjoy it. How about it?"

"Well-," Mr. Zeppelin still hesitated.

"You will go as my guest. You can be a visiting colleague, which you are. After seeing you in action the other night I have no doubt about your ability to handle yourself."

"Okay, it's a deal," said Mr. Zeppelin slapping his knees. "Acadamania, brace yourself. What do I wear?"

"Your baggiest tweeds so you won't be conspicuous. You can skip the monocle, though, tonight."

We arranged the time and place of meeting.

I met Mr. Zeppelin at the appointed hour at the front door of the Faculty Club. He had taken me literally and wore a baggy suit of Harris tweed. He looked like a huge shaggy bear-perfect attire for a faculty meeting. He was still slightly apprehensive, but this promptly disappeared when we ascended the stairs to the lounge where a gaggle of voices indicated a party in progress.

We paused in the doorway to look out at the throng. Clothes varied from dark conservative business suits to turtleneck sweaters. Tweed jackets with leather elbow guards were much in evidence. A quick inventory disclosed one hand-embroidered cossack shirt, one knee-length magenta smoking jacket, one poncho, one pair of cowboy boots and a variety of sandals, and one flat, Dutch-boy hat with a leather visor. Hair cuts ranged from crew cut to sheep dog. There was every variety of beard from Old Testament to early mandarin. It was a normal academic gathering.

"Great balls of fire," breathed Mr. Zeppelin. "It looks like a reunion of the Keystone Cops. These are the brains of the country?"

"It gives one to think, doesn't it?" I replied.

I introduced Mr. Zeppelin to the president who presented us in turn to Dr. Streiblatt, a short baldheaded man with thick glasses, who looked as if he didn't have a brain in his head. We exchanged pleasantries with him for a few minutes before moving on into the crowd.

"Well, sir," I said to Mr. Zeppelin, "you have just met a grade A, authentic genius."

"Who, the president?"

"No. Dr. Streiblatt."

"The little fat fellow? He seemed very ordinary and shy and modest."

"Only the truly great can afford to be modest. Everyone else here works on the premise that others will accord you the importance you attribute to yourself. It doesn't work, but that's the theory."

"I've seen it tried elsewhere."

"The president looks tired tonight," I said, pointing towards President Thorndike who was gazing out at the throng like a disillusioned bishop. "Being a university president these days is a tough assignment. It's like being a house detective in a Banff motel on a Saturday night. Let's get a drink."

As we wormed our way towards the bar I introduced Mr. Zeppelin to some of my colleagues along the way. He was warmly greeted by them and asked the usual inane questions about how he liked the country, the weather and the university, to which he replied in favourable terms. When we obtained our drinks we edged our way to a wall on which hung a picture which had apparently been painted by a spastic.

"I thought this would be a stag," said Mr. Zeppelin. "I see some ladies over there." He pointed his glass at two women shrieking at one another in a corner. One was wearing an unfortunate mini-skirt and the other, what appeared to be purple jodpurs.

"It is a stag. Those are female professors. Now you see why academic females contribute little genetic enrichment to the intelligence of future generations."

"Humph," grunted Mr. Zeppelin.

"They are, however, smart as hell."

"Intelligence in a female is an evolutionary blunder, like giving a crab an extra claw," he growled.

"Don't knock the house pets."

"Do they bite?"

"No. Come on over and meet them. I'll provide you with a theory of some kind and you can let them do the talking." We worked our way over to the corner.

"Ladies," I said, "let me introduce Professor Zeppelin, a visiting colleague. He would like to discuss with you his theory that totem poles are phallic symbols and are therefore Canadian equivalents to the onion domes on the Kremlin and the prows of Viking ships. Professor, these ladies are sociologists."

"Oh, wonderful," breathed the lady in the mini-skirt. Mr. Zeppelin bowed gallantly.

"I'll freshen our drinks," I said. As I headed for the bar I glanced over my shoulder. Both ladies were talking vigorously at the same time to a bemused Mr. Zeppelin. When I returned I was surprised to find him holding forth with both ladies hanging on his every word. I handed him his drink. As he paused to accept it, both his companions began baying like beagles. I wandered away.

After several minutes he rejoined me, smiling happily. "Those are two smart cookies," he said.

"Smart, yes. Cookies, no."

"Thanks for the ready-made theory, although it did seem an inappropriate subject to be discussing with ladies."

"No subject is improper in academic circles. Furthermore, women tend to be more daring than men."

"The ladies agreed with the theory completely. In fact, they extended it to include a bishop's mitre, the dangles on grain elevators, the Calgary Husky Tower, and violin bows. Indeed," he said thoughtfully, "they see a phallic symbol on everything except a man."

"Symbols are safer."

I could see a friend of mine, George Tweed, across the room. I waved to him. He returned my salute and threaded his way through the mob to join us. He was long and lanky with a bulbous nose and a brush-cut.

"Getting some free booze out of the university, I see," said George.

I introduced him to Mr. Zeppelin. "Professor Zeppelin is a visiting sociologist from abroad," I explained. "He is doing a comparative study of national characteristics, so I have undertaken to expose him to Canadian academic life in order to round out his impression of the Canadian identity. Would you tell him the theory you were expounding so brilliantly after golf the other day in the bar, about the dangers of professorial bumbling in public life."

"Gladly," said George. "My comments, Professor Zeppelin, had to do with Canadian professors sounding off when they are away from campus. I do not know what the situation is like abroad so my remarks will be applicable only to Canada. Professors tend to espouse causes, usually in an area they know nothing about. A professor speaks with considerable caution and conservatism about anything in his own field because first, he is recognized as an authority and bears some responsibility; and second, he is well aware of the limits of knowledge in his own discipline."

"But," George continued, "he will speak with great authority, bombast and irrationality on anything he is ignorant of. He uses academic freedom as a cloak for irresponsibility. Unfortunately, the public encourages this nonsense. It may be well known that Professor Smith is a prestigious, world-renowned authority in some area, so when he comments on any subject his word is accorded a respect which should be confined to his own sphere. Beware a professor speaking on any subject outside his narrow area of esoterica."

"I feel there is a good deal of validity to your thesis," said Mr. Zeppelin with a wry look in my direction. "I have observed examples which support it." I grinned at him.

"You see, George, I have been giving Professor Zeppelin my impression of Canadian life. He has a faint suspicion that I may be just a teeny bit biased in my appraisals. I would therefore like you to give him some of your less bizarre theories on publication, tenure and so forth. Carry on."

"He would be substituting one set of biases for another, but then a man without biases is a nonentity. My definition of tenure is that it is a charity run by the professors' union for the protection of the incompetent at governmental expense."

Mr. Zeppelin looked startled. "You have a union?" he asked, with a surprised look in my direction. I had the grace to be discomfited. I would explain to him later that our union was different.

"Yes, of course," said George. "The union would like to run the university on the democratic principle of consent and consensus. There's no chance of getting either. Now on the publish or perish bit, if a professor has anything worthwhile to say he will have it published. The only ones who complain are those who have nothing to say. However, those who have really nothing to offer frequently publish in order to add bibliographic scalps to their belts. There is a responsibility on professors, shamefully neglected, to maintain a noble reticence if they have nothing worth saying."

"Where does good teaching fit into the scheme of things?" enquired Mr. Zeppelin.

"The university works on the principle that the worst teachers are the best pedagogues," declaimed George. "The aim of the university is to develop independence and self-reliance in the students. If a prof is a lousy teacher the students will have to get the subject up on their own. It's good training for them."

"I think there's something wrong there someplace, but I can't quite put my finger on it," commented Mr. Zeppelin wryly.

"On publication credits, I should mention that a book of humour counts minus ten points," said George with a grin at me.

"Why is that?" asked Mr. Zeppelin. "I would expect the Canadian academic barnyard to cackle with wit."

"On the contrary. Professors operate on the basis that others will take you as seriously as you take yourself, which must therefore be very serious indeed. A sense of humour is disquieting because it arouses a suspicion that you are not taking other people as seriously as they think they should be taken. Pomposity requires solemnity; humbuggery and waggery are antagonistic."

"What else do Canadian academics do besides teach, research and admire one another?" asked Mr. Zeppelin, who was obviously enjoying himself thoroughly.

"Committee work. Any well-organized Canadian university is hagridden with committees. The function of such committees is to allow professors to impress one another; to deal with trivia which could be handled by a typist, grade II, to foster the kindly delusion that they are running the university; to do distasteful jobs which an administrator doesn't have the guts to do himself; and to stall for time till the problem disappears. Committees waste an inordinate amount of the time of able people who should be doing something useful." George took a long pull at his drink.

"There is a much-discussed proposal about these days as to how to solve this problem along with others afflicting Canadian universities. In simple terms the proposal suggests that new appointments of young staff are made at high salary with low status; that promotion to higher ranks with lower salary is based on age accelerated by incompetence; that senior professors would not be allowed to teach but would constitute a rich pool of incompetents from which would be drawn administrators and committees, areas where ability is not required. In this way, capable people will be left unhampered to undertake the useful functions of teaching and research, and the incompetents will be kept out of mischief. An ancillary advantage of using senior incompetents in administrative posts is that it would facilitate rapport with governments, since politicians are ill at ease in the presence of intellectual ability."

"The plan sounds eminently reasonable," said Mr. Zeppelin. "Do you think it will be adopted?"

"Probably not," said George. "Too sensible."

"Are you a scientist?" Mr. Zeppelin asked George.

"Yes, a chemist."

"Then I shall give you an opening by asking, what is science?"

"I shall rise to the challenge," said George. "Science is anything to which you can apply statistics. Interestingly enough, this assures that a scientist never tells the truth."

"How can that be?" said Mr. Zeppelin in surprise.

"Truth is absolute. Scientists establish by statistics that the variables they are working with are near the truth, but thereby prove that the data is not, strictly speaking, true. A philosopher, on the other hand, may be telling the truth or may not be. A scientist is always close to the truth, but never there; a philosopher may be there or a million miles away, no one knows. It is disquieting to find that philosophers spend most of their time proving that other philosophers are idiots. There is a good deal of evidence in support of this and it is generally accepted."

"I suspect that not all distortions of the truth emanate from philosophers," smiled Mr. Zeppelin.

George laughed. "You're absolutely right, Professor Zeppelin. Well, I must be slouching along so my department head will see me and know I've been here doing my duty. So long, Professor, happy hunting." George ambled off.

"A very interesting chap," said Mr. Zeppelin watching George's retreating figure.

"A sound thinker," I smiled.

"A fellow scientist. You hang together."

"If he's not careful he may get made a dean some day."

"What's a dean?"

"An executive drudge, bullied by the administration and maligned by the staff."

"What is an emeritus professor? I have heard the term used."

"Emeritus is a title costing nothing and meaning less. It is bestowed on retirement in lieu of an adequate pension."

Mr. Zeppelin swirled his drink around in his glass. "We are standing here studying the academic component of the Canadian identity," he mused, "but is there anything unique about them? Are they different from similar gatherings elsewhere, say in the U.S. or abroad?"

"Yes, they are."

"How?"

I scratched my nose. "Well, they're Canadian academics so they're different."

"In what way?"

"Most of them are Canadians so they therefore share the general qualities we have been trying to delineate. But more than that, they are part of an educational establishment which has distinctive features. It is not possible to divorce them from their operational milieu. Maybe it would help if you could see them in action in their councils and committees." I paused and thought about it.

"No, I withdraw that. Such meetings would mislead an outsider as they are frequently posturing charades. The same orators perform every time for their own delectation; echolalia is the order of the day; straw shibboleths are paraded to be defended or destroyed; there is much viewing with alarm; governments are damned and the administration deplored; matters of principle are seen under every bush and must be flushed out; nits are picked and hairs are split with delight. Surprisingly enough, when the wind has died down and the orators have lived up to their fond appreciation of themselves, the decisions taken are usually sound."

"By that you mean you agree with them."

"Not invariably. That's why I said usually."

"Quite." Mr. Zeppelin cocked an eyebrow at me. "How does a Canadian campus differ from an American one? They seem much alike to me."

"They are much alike because we are strongly influenced by the American system where many of us took our graduate work. This is counterbalanced by a retention of some of the European tradition. We are halfway between the stolidity of Europe and the diffusiveness of the States. We think we have the best of both worlds. American universities are more enamoured of facade than of substance. They tend to go for the razzle-dazzle of big names, Nobel Prize winners, and so on, but below that they can be very thin. These men bring prestige and big grant money and then spend their time tootling around the world. The quality of an American university is judged by the number of staff they have off-campus at any one time. Some American universities are subjected to considerable political interference. There is none of that in Canada, so far, and may it always continue. They are also much more influenced than we are by industrial impact and governmental contract finagling."

"How about the students? Are they different?"

"Canadian students, and staff too, tend to be more responsible and conservative. Again possibly a reflection of national characteristics. One factor which has had a marked influence on American universities is the fact that a much higher percentage of young people go on to university than is the case in Canada. Incidentally, it is much too low here. However, the great mass of students who enter the universities in the States brings in a great many who shouldn't be there at all by Canadian standards. These students, of course, avoid the sciences and more demanding traditional disciplines so the quality of these is usually quite good. The universities have had to develop programs which these kids can pass and hire staff who are prepared to pander to these requirements. As a result there has been a proliferation of programs in what seems to me as a traditionalist to be bizarre and frivolous subjects in a university curriculum."

"Well, I gather you feel Canadian universities compare favourably with those elsewhere," said Mr. Zeppelin.

"Yes, indeed," I answered haughtily.

"Good. I wouldn't have expected anything less of you."

"Let's go dip our goblets once again in the font of Minerva," I suggested, raising my glass.

"Good idea. Lead on."

We obtained fresh drinks and then withdrew to a corner of the room where it was relatively quiet. "A phut of professors, you observe, can be a jolly group when not busy splitting atoms or infinitives," I commented.

"Phut of professors?"

111

"I have suggested the term 'phut' as a composite noun for professors to correspond to a gaggle of geese or a density of deans. It is a proper word listed in the Oxford Dictionary, and you can't get more proper than that. There are two definitions given. One, the sound made by a bullet going by; and the other, the sound made by a bladder collapsing. So you take your choice."

Mr. Zeppelin laughed. "I know which one I'll take."

"So do I."

"Is there anything to the brain-drain to the south you hear about?"

"Yes, there is, unfortunately, but much less than previously. Our country must increase the opportunities available if we are to keep our best brains at home. That has been said so many times it is a cliché but not much is done about it. There is, however, a steady seepage back across the border of Canadians who have become fed up with the American rat-race and of Americans who are coming to Canada for the same reason. They are attracted here by the Canadian way of life and then try to change it."

"Yes, I've read about the large number of Yanks on our campuses. Is there any validity to this?"

"Yes, in some instances, particularly bumptious disciplines. However, it is desirable to have a sprinkling of staff from a variety of different environments - American, European, Asiatic. Excessive academic inbreeding fosters intellectual teratogenesis."

"Don't talk dirty," warned Mr. Zeppelin.

"I have been monopolizing your time," I said. "We should take full advantage of the opportunity for you to meet a variety of people. I think we should try to broaden your exposure in order to counterbalance the high science orientation you have been subjected to. Just wander around, join any group and ask a leading question, like what is truth. That will shake them up. Start off with that fellow over there with the bald head and shaggy eyebrows. He thinks any time he sits down he endows the chair. Whenever he talks to me he makes it clear that he is indulging in a conspicuous waste of time."

Mr. Zeppelin straightened up with a gleam in his eye. "I've had just enough courage out of that Courvoisier bottle to do it. Here I go. Watch for my body down stream."

"You will feel like Diogenes in Bedlam, but good luck."

Mr. Zeppelin sidled off. For the next half hour I followed his progress from group to group and noted the vigorous discussions which erupted soon after his arrival. Finally he rejoined me in a corner of the room. "Boy," he grinned. "I haven't been so happy since I found a full bottle of rye in a trash can."

"That would pose a nice problem in ethics. What did you do?"

"Drank it, of course. Maybe they were trying to kick the habit."

"Nice rationalization. Well, had enough for one night, Professor? Shall we shake the mud of Parnassus from our feet?"

"Yes, I'm ready to go. My head's all awhirl. We'll sort it out tomorrow."

CHAPTER TEN

Throw the Torch—Quick

Mr. Zeppelin was a little late arriving next morning. I waited impatiently as I was anxious to get his reactions to the previous night's junket. When he finally arrived and we were settled down I asked him how he had enjoyed himself.

"Very much. It was very interesting," he said slowly, licking the beer foam lovingly from his mustache. "It was quite an experience to wander in the redolent fields of sage and meet the brainy component of the Canadian identity." He pulled his lower lip thoughtfully, shaking his head.

"Somewhat shattering?" I asked.

"To a certain extent. Brains come in some pretty strange packages, I must say."

"Don't confuse brains with education. Those people are all well-educated but some are pretty dumb. It's a paradox of academic life that a person can be brainy and stupid at the same time. They're specialists who know a great deal about not much; yet not much about a great deal. It is possible to get a degree with one's carapace of ignorance intact."

"Hmm. That helps."

"Also don't confuse erudition with wisdom. The two are not synonymous, although not necessarily antagonistic. It is possible, even common, to be learned but not wise."

"And wise but not learned?"

"Yes. Wisdom comes more from the heart than from the brain. Advanced degrees tend to cause atrophy of the heart. When learning produces arrogance, wisdom dies; but when knowledge produces humility, wisdom is born."

"Good. I feel much better about life." He stretched his arms over his head. "One thing that puzzles me," he continued, "is the nature of some of the programs offered. One of the groups I got involved in last night was talking about courses in sandpile management and in underwater basket weaving. What are they?"

I laughed. "Figures of speech. Mickey Mouse courses. Sandpile management is taught in the Physical Education Department; underwater basket weaving in Commerce."

"I see. I guess. What are some of the other disciplines? Everyone knows what physics is, or chemistry, or mathematics, but how about some of the others?"

"Where shall I start? How about sociology, which is the cataloguing of the obvious. Sociology delineates togetherness; psychology explains why it doesn't work; and psychiatry picks up the pieces. Anthropology says man is an animal; theology says he is a soul. The former is supported by biology and history; the latter by witchcraft and sophism."

"Do you have departments of witchcraft and sophism on the campus?"

"Not under those titles."

"Carry on, Professor."

"Very well. If politics is the art of the possible, then statistics is the art of the probable; theology is the art of the improbable and philosophy, the art of the impossible."

"You didn't pop those off the top of your head. Who are you quoting?"

"Myself. Self-quotation is a form of intellectual onanism indulged in by academics."

"Your favourite author, I'm sure."

"Now tell me," I urged, "how did you make out last night in your search for truth? I'm very anxious to know."

"It was all very confusing and amusing." He started to chuckle and then laughed with his usual deep 'huff, huff, huff'. "It was great fun. There was no agreement on what truth is or where it is to be found, as was to be expected, but the variations are limitless. One intense individual with a red beard claimed that truth is inimical to the best interests of mankind because all the complex inter-relationships developed by man are based upon deceit; thus truth would be disruptive. Another, in the same vein, said that truth would be a searchlight disclosing the unacceptable. Truth must be stamped out.

"One character stated that the best example of immutable, constant, permanent truth is to be found in the stupidity of the campus parking authority. He supported this with a good deal of evidence and feeling. The man with the eyebrows said truth is dead and should be left to rot in peace. One of the younger groups agreed that ultimate truth is sex. I shall not sully your gentle ears, Professor, with the fascinating data in support of this thesis. One morose individual said truth could only be found in the bottom of a bottle. He had obviously been seeking diligently for truth during the course of the evening.

"One person said the closest approach to the purity of truth which man could reach was listening to a fine symphony orchestra. One of his associates said a good Dixieland band came a lot closer. When this debate became heated I left. A youngish fellow in a turtleneck sweater said man could only approach truth through drugs. He described a trip he had been on and while he had certainly been off in the wild blue yonder, I doubt if he came any closer to the truth. He certainly hadn't brought any back with him, that's for sure. One hard-nosed prof said the only reliable certitude was money.

"One guy in a purple vest said, in a superior way, that he himself had written the definitive book on the subject of truth and referred me to his publisher. I got to hell out of there pretty fast I can tell you.

"Another individual said truth was beauty. I thought we were on to something there but when I asked him for an example he said aces back to back."

"Did anybody ask you for your definition?" I asked.

"Only once. Everybody else was too busy giving their versions."

"What did you say?"

"I said that truth could only be found in garbage. Huff, huff." He laughed happily. "This was considered terribly clever and got quite a round of applause. In retrospect I've decided it was, too."

"I'm inclined to agree." I raised my stein. "Well here's to truth, whatever and wherever it is." We saluted the illusive goddess.

Mr. Zeppelin sat in deep thought for several minutes. "I find my exposure to academania rather disconcerting. I realize that cocktail party yatter can be deceiving, but I gain the impression from last night and elsewhere that the Canadian universities may have forgotten their purpose."

"Nonsense," I responded. "We haven't forgotten anything. We are doing the same thing we always have."

"Maybe that's the problem. Maybe doing the same thing isn't good enough. Now I know what the kids mean when they talk about relevance."

"I don't mean we teach the same things, for heaven's sake. Courses change every year to accommodate the flood of new knowledge."

"But your purpose has not changed?"

"No, certainly not."

"Maybe it should."

"I don't see anything wrong."

"You'd better have another look."

I stared at him in bewilderment. Finally I asked, "Do you think the Canadian educational system deficient?"

"It's admirably adapted for its present purpose - reinfection with the same old virus. Same set of values, same attitudes, same limitations, same vision."

"Sort of an autointoxication?"

"I thought that was carbon monoxide poisoning. However it'll do. That's why the students are opting for fresher air outside the university. They're questioning your set of values and trying to find themselves."

"That old wheeze. I never knew anyone yet who set out to find themselves who found anything worth finding. If they have to look there's nothing to find."

"Like the Canadian identity?" asked Mr. Zeppelin.

That rather shook me. "I hope not. However, a sense of personal identity is to be found in accomplishment. This requires hard work. The last place these drop-outs would think of looking for themselves is in hard work. They'll look in bars, brothels, drugs and star-gazing but never in work."

"The old work ethic, huh?"

"What's wrong with that?"

"Nothing as far as I know but it seems to be out of fashion."

"Not with most young people, fortunately."

"Don't you think a university education should have some relevance to the Canadian scene, to the needs of society, to the–,"

"It does, that's my point."

"Oh, I guess I missed it." Mr. Zeppelin leaned back and stretched. "I remember when I was studying law at the University of Ashloops–,"

"Hold it," I said, raising my hand. "I happen to know the University of Ashloops doesn't have a law faculty."

"Quite true. That's why I quit." Mr. Zeppelin smiled sweetly. "The only gem I took away from a year's study there was that yak milk is pink. You'd be surprised how hard it is to work that into a conversation. Now that I have succeeded I feel my time there was not wasted. At any rate, I decided I wanted a more challenging course so I enrolled in a program in pomegranate picking at Blossom University in the southern part of the province. This was a new university and like all new ones it was dedicated to the introduction of courses not offered elsewhere. When I was graduated from the program, magnum cum laudanum, I had difficulty getting a job. So did those from the programs in pearl diving and olive stuffing. When I complained to my professor about my inability to get a job he got quite huffy and said the course was offered for its cultural content. He said a university pursued knowledge for the sake of knowledge. Would you agree, Professor?"

"Yes, of course," I replied. "If a person wants a practical course he should go to a trade school."

"You don't think the courses offered at a university should have some relationship to employment opportunities and the needs of society?"

"Certainly not. It would be stultifying to academic freedom and scholarly pursuit. The university takes no responsibility for jobs."

"Hmm. I see. Well, I was offered a job of sorts. Since I had done well in the basic course, my professor wanted me to go on for graduate work in promegranate picking with a view to joining his staff later. He was very enthusiastic about the future of his department and was keen to begin a graduate program. Indeed, since that time he has been very successful. He has been able to introduce courses in pomegranate picking into the high schools and is now pressuring to get them into the public schools. There is therefore a great demand for people with advanced training in pomegranate picking to teach other scholars in the field, both for university and secondary school employment. There are also courses to be taught on how to teach pomegranate picking to those who are going to teach pomegranate picking." Mr. Zeppelin heaved a great sigh. "It's a pity I didn't continue in this new and dynamic field."

"You have made your point," I said in a surly voice. "However, it must be recognized that some degree of specialization is necessary in view of the vast and complex fund of knowledge which must be dealt with today. Now you take my research on the kidney function of the octopus-,"

"The kidney function of the octopus? You must be kidding."

"Other people's research interests, like other people's love affairs are always inexplicable."

"What has the kidney function of the octopus got to do with the price of rape in Alberta-the grain that is?"

"Nothing. It comes under the heading of basic research which-,"

"How basic can you get before you disappear from sight entirely? For once the government has my sympathy." Mr. Zeppelin banged down his hands on the arms of his chair. I decided not to pursue the tenuous arguments in support of basic research. I would wait for a more propitious moment, such as when I was discussing the matter with other people in basic research.

I changed directions. "Youth is the time of preparation for the future. Youth is therefore-,"

"When I think back to my youth, lo these many years," Mr. Zeppelin interrupted, "my regrets are not for the mistakes I made but for the opportunities for fun and deviltry which I passed up, particularly in the sexual sphere. It has been my observation that the happiest old men are the dirty old men. A basis for this has to be established early in life."

"Well, what is your opinion of modern Canadian youth?"

"I think they're wonderful. Why don't you let them run the university like they want to?"

"They'd do as good a job as the professors, that's for sure!" I admitted. "But running a university is a lousy, difficult job. The students would be happy to give it back again if they ever got it. They serve a more useful job in giving the university a hot foot."

"The only young people who bother me are the shaggy-haired creeps in the weird clothes you see about," complained Mr. Zeppelin.

"Oh, come now," I said. "Hair styles are just a fad. Long hair and beards happen to be the 'in' thing at the moment; clothes are a matter of fashion. I'll bet you wore sideburns and bell-bottom cords."

"Sure, I did. I don't really care how a guy dresses or wears his hair if he's prepared to work. But a lot of these kooks are indicating by their kookiness that they're not prepared to work. They figure the world owes them a living and it doesn't. The world owes nobody nothing unless he's prepared to work for it."

"Your generation gap is showing," I said severely.

"There should be a generation gap or I haven't learned anything in the last twenty-five years. You too, Professor."

"Maybe we've learned the wrong things."

"The kids these days are too premacocious. They want to grow up too quickly. But my principal objection is to the few who insist on being dirty. That's a particularly unfortunate method of protest in my book. The stench-set turns me off. In my profession I am subjected to quite a variety of noxious aromas but I don't want to meet them socially."

"I agree with you but-,"

"Some of these kids make my garbage pails smell like roses. All the so-called lower animals are clean, with the exception of pigs, who have picked up some slovenly habits from the Irish."

"Hey now, watch it. Some of my ancestors came from County Antrim."

"Don't get excited, Professor, so did some of mine." I had long since given up trying to keep track of his geneology.

"I have a strong taint of Irish in me also, and it's through that branch of the family my Spanish blood comes." He looked at me expectantly so I rose to the bait.

"Spanish? How do you account for that?"

"One of my ancestors fell off a Spanish galleon when the Invisible Armada was going by. He married a beautiful Irish girl, a direct descendant of Brian Boru, and established a dynasty in Donegal, which indeed is named after him. He was called Don by the natives since they couldn't pronounce the last part of his name."

"I suppose he was a Spanish grandee."

"Of course. He had a soap factory in Castille but he got put out of business and had to join the army. The power for his factory came from a windmill. One day along came a tall, skinny knight in armour who charged the windmill. It wrecked the knight but also wrecked the windmill. Pity."

"Yes, wasn't it. But to return to the youth of today."

"Ah, yes, that group to whom we shall throw the torch-flame

first. And let's throw it quick, before we burn our fingers."

"What do you think of the drug cult?"

"I'm all for it. If it wasn't for Amphogel I couldn't survive."

"No. I mean marijuana and that sort of thing."

"I'm against it."

"Good. So am I. What should be done about it?"

"Have you ever noticed that if you stroke a cat's tail he will purr, but if you hold onto his tail he will pull away and scream bloody murder."

"So?"

"Blessed if I know. But I always felt there was some great philosophical truth to be learned from it."

"Well, how are we to get the younger generation away from drugs?"

"Oh, I have the solution to that."

"You do?" I said in surprise. "I would be very interested to hear it."

"Return sex to its position of pre-eminence in sybaritic dalliance," he declaimed loudly, holding up his hand in a commanding gesture.

"Hurrah," I cried, not at all sure what I was cheering for.

He lowered his hand and continued in a conspiratorial tone. "The solution rests with the girls. Women are the custodians of civilization. It was women who coaxed men down out of the trees to start the whole thing in the first place. It is they who forced man into the unnatural setting of a family nest, because the male has no nesting instinct. If they can do that they can do anything. Their power is boundless. The solution to drugs is to make sex again the peak of voluptuosity. The use of drugs is largely a protest against accepted norms, so if we can return sex to its role as the ultimate joy and no-no, then who will look to drugs? The boys aren't about to change the situation, so it's up to the girls. If the girls will just make it tougher to score the problem is solved." He spread out both hands palm up.

"Lysistrata rides again," I cried. "The battle is joined."

"The powder-puff is mightier than the sword," proclaimed Mr. Zeppelin. Don't shoot till you can see the whites of their undies."

I paused. "How are you going to sell this to the girls?" I asked.

He leaned back in his chair. "I've given you the solution. It's up to you to put it into operation."

"Thanks a lot."

CHAPTER ELEVEN

It's a Long Way to Halifax

Mr. Zeppelin gazed fondly at the foam on his beer before tossing it off with a polite 'salud'. I said 'chimo' as I joined him. The amenities having been taken care of, Mr. Zeppelin leaned back, relaxed luxuriously with his hands behind his head and asked, "Which what of the big what are we on today?"

"I would like to have a look at the effect which geography and ethnic factors have on our identity," I responded. "Canada is a huge land mass stretching from-,"

Mr. Zeppelin blew out his lips. "You can skip that part. I'll concede that it's a long way to walk from Vancouver to Halifax with a bucket of water on your head."

"I was just stating the obvious as a point of departure," I stated testily.

"Just holler, all aboard, and away we go."

"Very well," I said snappishly. I was annoyed with him for cutting off the eloquent introduction I had planned.

"It is a well-known fact that the physical environment influences the behaviour of animals, including humans. The beauty of our country is bound to have a salubrious effect upon the Canadian personality."

Mr. Zeppelin looked unconvinced. "Humans can be sordid in beautiful surroundings and noble in squalor."

"True, but that is spitting up wind. In general, behaviour is conditioned by the stimulus."

"Canadians are so conditioned to beauty they don't even see it."

"Yet unconsciously the stimulus is present. Wherever one lives in Canada one is surrounded by beauty. From the rolling plains of Saskatchewan to-,"

Mr. Zeppelin began making motions as if he were playing a violin, humming *This Land is My Land.*

"Saskatchewan does have a beauty of its own," I said defensively.

"So does a hippopotamus. An appreciation of Saskatchewan beauty is a cultivated depravity, like drinking Irish whisky." He grinned impishly at me.

"Well, I think pride in the beauty of our magnificent country is one aspect of the Canadian personality."

Mr. Zeppelin pursed his lips. "Yes, I'll agree to that. My only reservation was that beauty of surroundings does not assure purity of soul."

"Very well. Your reservation is noted. Now, what other effects does geography have on the several components of the Canadian identity?"

"For one thing, you don't find Eskimos sitting on the stock exchange in Toronto. Incidentally, one of my great, great grand-mothers was an Eskimo. She put paprika in her seal meat paté and made quite a reputation for herself as an avant-garde cook in the area."

"I've lost track of your ancestors, you've had so many apparently," I said sarcastically. I was still in a bit of ill-temper.

"More than most," he allowed, "And approximately half of them have been women." He grinned disarmingly at me.

"Humph. Canada does have a frontier spirit which lends validity, aggressiveness and daring to our personality which you don't find in older, more effete countries," I went on, warming up to my subject.

"I remember Joe Sporlikc," said Mr. Zeppelin meditatively. "He had so much daring that he went out one night and froze to death. Too bad, he was an expert snooker player." Mr. Zeppelin looked very sad.

"It takes courage to go out to brave the elements in the wilds of this country," I said sharply.

"It happened in Calgary and he was drunk at the time," said Mr. Zeppelin.

"Damn it," I exclaimed. "You're not letting me get very far with the brave frontier bit. I was going to wax eloquent on our heritage, our struggle with the wilderness, our simple virtues of truth and courage, and all that stuff."

"Save your wind to cool your parritch, as my Scottish aunt used to say. We've heard it all before. I'll grant you that all Canadians are basically brave-hearted frontiersmen. You need only attend a Grey Cup match or try to cross a street in Montreal at rush hour to recognize that fact. Where do we go from there?"

"You're being somewhat obstructionist this morning," I complained. "I've lost my train of thought."

"Just holler all aboard again and we'll start over."

"All right. Then let's charge into the Quebec situation."

"Oh, that's no great problem," said Mr. Zeppelin with a grand wave of the hand.

"It isn't?" I said, surprised.

"No. The French Canadians are just trying to do what you and I are trying to do-establish a Canadian identity. The only difference is that they are doing something about it instead of just talking. After all, they're one of the two founding races-not a junior partner-and they're as interested in establishing an identity as we are. We should be grateful to them because our French population provides something unique to Canada. We have commented previously about Canada's concern that she be different from the United States. Our Frenchiness provides it, even if nothing else does. The Quebecers are helping Canada build a special identity."

"But aren't they divisive?"

"No. Their efforts will continue to be within the Canadian framework."

"How about the talk about separatism?"

"Not significant as long as they are allowed and encouraged to develop their contribution to the Canadian identity within a flexible and sensible framework."

"Some of them apparently take separatism very seriously- bombs and all that."

"Every group has a lunatic fringe. But firebrands sometimes provide a heat by which sensible people can bake a cake."

"Do you condone violence?" I demanded severly.

"No, I don't. And neither do the ninety-nine point nine percent of sensible Quebecers either. The threat of separation is a tactic of diversion, like pointing at the moon while you're picking a guy's pocket. Quebec has done pretty well with this strategy in Ottawa. All they're asking, as I see it, is an opportunity to make the unique contribution to Canada that they know they can if allowed."

"Who's stopping them?"

"Nobody, really, but they don't know it. Things will simmer down when they find that out." Mr. Zeppelin tugged thoughtfully at his mustache.

"The French are a proud race, and with good reason. They're fine people with a great history and tradition. Every guy should be proud of his background or he's no man at all. You're proud of being Scottish-Irish; I'm proud of my mixed lineage; and so should every Canadian, whether his ancestry was English, Ukrainian, Chinese or Dutch. It's all right to be proud but you've got to let the other guy be proud, too. That's where we've failed with our Indians, but that's another can of pemmican we won't open now. You can't squelch a guy's pride or you are in trouble. And the same goes for ethnic or other groups. And for nations. Hey, I'm really wound up today." Mr. Zeppelin held a fist aloft.

"You're doing fine. Carry on, Canada," I urged.

Mr. Zeppelin frowned in concentration. "Patriotism has become sort of old-hat today, which is a pity. There's no reason why a man shouldn't love his country. I think it's a creditable emotion. The thing is, as with people, you've got to let the other guy be just as proud of his country as you are of yours. Let him have his pride, whether you agree or not. As the old Indian chief said, 'If all man think alike, every man want my squaw'. A fine plea for tolerance."

"Now you're talking like a nationalist. Nationalism is outmoded. We're all part of one community, the world. We have to work together and help each other."

"Agreed, completely. But the United Nations isn't yet a family picnic. It's an assembly of nations, each with their prides. I say respect their prides as equals."

"Some are more equal than others."

"Not in their prides they're not."

I chewed my pen for a few minutes. "How is Canada going to melt the two founding cultures into an entity; how eliminate the animosity which unfortunately has developed?"

Mr. Zeppelin scratched his head. "People have got to get to know one another, then the animosities disappear. But Canada is so bloody big it's hard to bring it about. The government's got to increase its efforts to promote visits back and forth. Hey, I've got an idea." He sat up straight. "The government should provide a dowry to any girl who marries across the cultures, either way. How about that?"

"In the old days they used to send out shiploads of brides for the settlers. Something like that?"

"Yes. Trainloads of brides backwards and forwards across Canada. Wonderful. Think of the excitement."

"Women's lib would object."

"Then trainloads of men, too. Sure, why not?"

"An imaginative proposal but I foresee some technical difficulties. I think a more subtle approach is called for. If your earlier idea of cross visitation is implemented then nature may accomplish the rest."

"Okay, then how about a rock festival in Vancouver which can only be attended by males from the West and females from the East; and one in Montreal with the reverse arrangement; then the following year switch it around? Talk about Opportunities for Youth. That ought to stir up the old melting pot. Eh what?"

"It would stir up more than that I'm afraid."

"Poof. Have you no romance in your soul?"

"Maybe, but it's not turned on by an electric guitar at a shattering decibel level."

"*Sweet Sue* on the ukelele is no longer the language of love, Professor."

"Speaking of language," I said, trying to get the conversation into more constructive fields, "where do you stand on the two official languages in Canada?"

"No problem that time won't take care of," he answered expansively.

"How do you mean?"

Mr. Zeppelin lowered his voice to a whisper, looking over his shoulder melodramatically to see if anyone was listening. Only Robespierre, who was sound asleep, was within earshot.

"What I have to say will not endear me to my French-speaking colleagues, I'm afraid," he said in low tones. "The problem, if there is one, which I doubt, is fleeting and transistoral. It doesn't matter what language you use to talk to your neighbour across the back fence, whether it's French, Spanish or Italian, but when you get out into the market place you've got to communicate with your customers. I've travelled around the world enough to have observed that English has gradually become the international language, le Grande Charles notwithstanding."

"Yes, I've noticed that too," I agreed. "I wonder why."

"The English were too dumb to learn another language; the Americans too lazy; and the Canadians both. Anyhow, now it's a fact of international life. People from various countries know that if they are going to be involved in international affairs, commercial or otherwise, English will be understood by most of the people they meet, so they learn it. Also, looking farther ahead, they have their kids learn English in schools. Except France." Mr. Zeppelin leaned forward earnestly.

"The principal reason that France opposed Britain's admission to the Common Market was linguistic, not economic. The French know very well that the representatives of all the other countries will speak English, since everyone there will understand it-including the French, although they will pretend they don't."

"What's this got to do with Canada?" I asked.

"There's no way a small group on this continent can avoid English, except for local chit-chat."

"Do you think it's wrong then to promote two languages in Canada?"

"No, there's nothing wrong with promoting it. But for cultural, not political reasons. Also bilingualism can't be accomplished by legislation. Language is not a good political weapon. Language is a means of communication and will follow whatever direction is the most useful and versatile. Ergot, English is in."

"One thing I've noticed abroad," I commented, "is that foreigners usually speak a better brand of English than do many of the English."

"Gore bloimey, Professor 'iggins, yer'ave 'it the nile on the 'ead with the 'ammer roit orf," said Mr. Zeppelin.

"Certainly it is easier to understand a Swede speaking English than someone from Lancashire or Soho or Glasgow. The English say snootily that the Swede speaks BBC English which is a synthetic brand. Surprisingly enough, the Swede, or Dutch or whatever, has less trouble understanding a Canadian than he does many Englishmen. It may be that eventually international English will become a language of its own, like Latin in its heyday. Indeed this has happened to a considerable extent already."

"No language will be popular or longlasting which insists on giving a sex to inanimate nouns. It is an absurd intrusion of sex into inappropriate areas. One of the strengths of English, and the reason for the declension of Latin."

I ignored this side path. "It is paradoxical that the English language may be saved by foreigners from the depredations of the English on their own language. And of the Americans." I added.

Mr. Zeppelin laughed. "Sho nuff, mushmouth. Y'all ain't whistling Dixie."

I smiled at him. "Regional dialects are, of course, a common phenomenon. But it is surprising that, in a tiny island the size of Britain, such diverse dialects could have been maintained for hundreds of years."

Mr. Zeppelin grunted. "Perversity."

"The States," I went on, "is much larger so it is not surprising that regional linguistic barbarisms have developed. The total effect is that the States is polluting its language almost as fast as its environment."

"But Canada will save the day for linguistic purity. Hurrah," cried Mr. Zeppelin waving an imaginary flag. "The best of British luck to you, mate."

"Thank you," I smiled, "I may need it. Canadians do have certain linguistic traits which distinguish them from Americans."

"Like good grammar?"

"That, too. But what I had in mind is the peculiarly Canadian tendency to sprinkle our conversation with 'ehs' in sort of an interrogatory fashion. I suppose it is spelled with an e but we pronounce it 'ay' with a long a."

"We do, eh?"

"Yes. You get the point. The use of 'eh' is so characteristically Canadian that Americans frequently use it to identify Canadians. Any time they hear an 'eh' in a conversation they say 'aha, a Canadian'. And most Canadians don't even realize they use the word. It has been suggested that 'eh' is apologetic but Canadians don't see it that way. At any rate, while 'eh' is not particularly euphonious, it is better than the American equivalent of 'huh'."

"You think so, huh?"

"Another linguistic difference from the Americans is our pronunciation of the last letter of the alphabet which we call 'zed' and they call 'zee'. This disqualifies some American advertising in Canada although they don't know it, like Ee-Z soapflakes or Lay-Z rocking chairs."

Mr. Zeppelin held up a fist. "We shall fight to our last philologist to hang onto our zed, by golly, it's all we have left." He lowered his fist. "Other words the Americans say we pronounce differently are 'house' and 'about'. They say we pronounce them 'hoose' and 'aboot' although to our ear they seem to be saying 'hause' and 'abaout'. I suppose it depends to some extent what part of Canada the person comes from since the 'hoose' and 'aboot' bit probably derives from the Scottish."

I thought that over. "Surprisingly enough, although Canada is very large, we don't really have marked regional variations in English.

"However," I continued, "the Newfies have a delightful brogue traceable to ancestry, as well as some marvellous expressions, like 'stay where you're to till I come where you're at!' To a Newfy all lakes are called ponds, such as Pond Superior. I asked a friend of mine from Newfoundland what, then, was a lake. He said 'a lake's what you have when there's a hole in your boot'. Something of the same Scottish-Irish background is detectable in Bluenoses, other barnacle-bottoms and in the Ottawa valley natives. Aside from these variations, a Canadian from Vancouver speaks much like one from Toronto."

"Except that the Vancouverite talks through his hat and the Torontonian, down his nose."

I laughed. "Only Albertans speak the truth."

"Sure. Ask any Albertan. Vancouverites are not too bad. After all they are westerners. But Torontonians are Canadian Bostonians. They think Canada stops at their city limits."

"Torontonians are somewhat parochial it is true-,"

"I don't care about their religion," Mr. Zeppelin interrupted, "but what makes me mad is that the East seems to think the West has been provided for their benefit. They take our stuff, manufacture it and send it back at a big profit. If we get obstreperous they pressure the government into screwing us up with freight rates."

"I'm afraid it just makes economic sense to do most of the manufacturing in the East where the preponderence of population is concentrated."

"I say we should do more manufacturing in the West and exploit the East, dad burnit. We should, at least, charge more for our stuff and equivocate the balance of payments. The East gets fat on the West. I say we should share the obesity."

"Look who's talking," I said, pointing at his huge stomach.

Mr. Zeppelin laughed. "Figure of speech only, my dear sir." He patted his paunch affectionately. "But the West's the best."

"The easterners say westerners are snobs but I disagree."

"What do you mean by a snob?"

I thought this over. "A snob is someone whose pretensions you don't share," I suggested.

"Very good, Mr. Webster."

"I wonder what the dictionary says," I mused. "I'll go get one so we can see if westerners really are snobs." I brought a dictionary from the house while Mr. Zeppelin poured us each another beer. I leafed through the book.

"Here we are, humm. There are several definitions. We'll apply them one at a time to westerners to see if we qualify as snobs. First, 'a person who behaves with servility to social superiors'. How about that?"

Mr. Zeppelin pulled at his lower lip. "A westerner recognizes no social superiors, so how can he be accused of toadying to someone who doesn't exist?"

"Very good," I agreed. "We have disposed of that one. Second definition, 'one with exaggerated respect for social position or wealth'."

"As I implied a moment ago, westerners do not accept stratification in the social order so the question is not relevant. As far as wealth is concerned, we respect a man for his money if he got it honestly and on his own merits. There's no taint in respecting an honest man. Also, in the West there is no need to exaggerate."

"Not so conclusive, but I'll accept it." I said judiciously. "Next, 'one who judges merit by externals'."

"Hmmm. What the hell else can you use. You can't see a guy's pancreas and even if you could I'm not at all sure it would provide a better criterion of his worth than what you can see. Westerners judge a man by what he is and how he behaves; not by his ancestry or school tie. If you're supposed to judge a guy by internals, by looking up his er, um, credentials, then we'll let the easterners bring up the rear. As usual."

"It looks as if we flunked that one, I'm afraid."

"A bad definition. That dictionary must have been written by an easterner."

I held up the book for his inspection. "He went to Oxford."

Mr. Zeppelin nodded knowingly. "It figures."

"The last definition is 'or is ashamed of socially inferior connections'."

"Poof," said Mr. Zeppelin airily. "That doesn't apply to westerners. Many of us have relatives living in the East and we don't fuss about it. We may be sorry for them but certainly not ashamed. If they would just smarten up enough to come west many of them might turn out all right. Indeed, many westerners came from the East originally. If their qualities were good and their hearts were pure they were able to make the transition. In some cases, though, it takes a couple of generations. A westerner, on the other hand, is impervious to contamination and can never become an easterner, unless he marries one, and then God help him."

I shut the dictionary with a bang. "I take it then that we are agreed: westerners are proud, superior and charitable to those so unfortunate as not to be westerners. But snobs? Never."

CHAPTER TWELVE

The Grass Roots

The next morning Mr. Zeppelin and Robespierre stayed only long enough to toss off a stein of beer.

"Can't linger today, Professor," said Mr. Zeppelin. "This is our big day with the weekend coming up and we're a bit behind in our orders."

I was disappointed. "I'm sorry to hear that. I was looking forward to another session, possibly dealing with the armed forces."

"I tell you what," said Mr. Zeppelin. "Tomorrow would be a good night for us to go to the beer parlor like we've talked about.

Give you a chance to see Canada's grass roots. How about it?"

"Yes. I would be delighted."

"Good. I'll pick you up about eight o'clock."

"I could get there on my own."

"No need, and parking is nasty in that area."

"Where will we be going?"

"The Rondo Hotel. It's got four bedrooms and four acres of beer parlor. Biggest tap room in western Canada. Have you been to a beer parlor lately?"

"No. Not since I was an undergraduate and that's more years ago than I care to admit. What do I wear?"

Mr. Zeppelin laughed. "Your motorboat and gown so you won't be conspicuous. See you tomorrow evening, Professor." He turned and roared at Robespierre. "Come, Apollo. Hitch up Pegasus and we'll take off for the river Stynx."

Mr. Zeppelin called for me Saturday evening in a delapidated, old Volkswagon. It was quite a sight to see him fold his great bulk in and out of the little car.

"Isn't this thing a little tight in the armpits for you?" I asked.

"I gave my chauffeur the Rolls for the evening," he explained. "He's taking Lady Cynthia to a crumpet festival at Claridge's and wanted to put on a bit of swank."

We took off like a startled chipmunk.

"Open the door and drag your foot on the corners, the brakes aren't too good," he directed, as he noted me grimly hanging on to the seat. We zipped our way along through the traffic.

"When we meet the boys, I'll try to stick-handle the conversation along the lines you are interested in," he said. "I'd suggest you don't tell them you're a professor. It might put them off. Frankly they don't have too high an opinion of professors. Figure they're drones in the hive." He grinned sideways at me. "For tonight, Merv, you are a visiting colleague from abroad-like, maybe Regina."

"Okay, Barney Oldfield."

"That dates you, Professor."

We arrived at the hotel more by luck than skill. The parking lot contained hundreds of cars parked every which way. After finding a vacant spot we made our way to the door of the beer parlor. As we entered the room I stopped in amazement. The place was huge. It was filled with people sitting at small tables which were loaded with beer bottles and glasses. His estimate of four acres wasn't far off. There was a loud hum of happy voices and cheerful laughter.

"Good heavens," I cried. "Where did they all come from?"

"We working people live a fairly circumcised life," said Mr. Zeppelin. "Just blood, sweat and beers."

"I had no idea that beer was such a popular drink."

"That's only part of it. They come for companionship-togetherness, I guess, is the modern term," explained Mr. Zeppelin.

"How can you have togetherness in the middle of a football stadium?"

"Every table is an island unto itself; but the togetherness is fortified by the nearness of the others." He was looking out over the throng.

"There are my gang over yonder." His wave was answered by a wave from a distant corner. "Follow me," he directed. We picked our way cautiously between the tables. As we went along Mr. Zeppelin was greeted by innumerable people with cheerful insults and friendly quips. He returned the greetings in a like vein. We arrived at our table where we were warmly welcomed by his friends. After a bit of scrounging two more chairs were located. Mr. Zeppelin introduced me to his four friends.

Mike was the oldest of the group, in his fifties, with stiff grey hair and a heavy, deeply creased face. Roscoe and Fred would be in their forties. Roscoe was thin and dark with bright, sharp eyes and a crooked nose. Fred, in contrast, had thin blondish hair and heavy lidded eyes. The fourth member was called Speed, which seemed an unlikely name for him, as he was rather slow and languid. He was in his thirties with long hair hanging over his shirt collar. They all called Mr. Zeppelin Zep, so I did the same.

"Mike here," said Mr. Zeppelin pointing with his beer glass, "is a chief in the local Ukrainian Mafia. He's a fence for hot holubchies."

"You overgrown blimp," said Mike cheerfully.

"Hey, Zep, did you make a big clean-up in the financial district today?" asked Speed.

"Sure did," answered Mr. Zeppelin, "but it was all in Spanish espositos. I'm going to start a hockey team."

"Then you can afford to buy a round," said Fred. "Stop stalling around, Zep." Since the table was already covered with bottles this seemed hardly necessary.

"Not Zep," interjected Roscoe. "He's tight as-,"

"No, he ain't," objected Speed. "He'd give you the shirt off his back, soup stains and all."

"You could make a tent out of it," I said, trying to make a contribution.

"It would draw flies," complained Fred.

Mr. Zeppelin obviously enjoyed being the butt of the jibes. He beamed around happily. "Enjoying yourself, Merv?" he asked.

"Haven't enjoyed myself so much since I split two infinitives in one sentence."

The conversation took a sudden switch to a discussion of the chances of the local football team in the up-coming football season. Everyone participated with enthusiasm and, as far as I could tell, considerable knowledge.

"The team would do all right if the front office would leave them alone," complained Fred.

"I hear they've signed a new half-back," commented Zep.

"Is that so?" said Speed eagerly. "Who?"

"Joe Scrotum. They say he's just a natural ball-carrier." Mr. Zeppelin huffed happily.

"Twenty years a cowboy and he still steps in them," observed Roscoe shaking his head sadly. Speed thumbed his nose. The conversation continued about football with a consensus emerging that our chances were none too good, due mainly to the dummies in the front office. Beer continued to arrive in huge quantities. After considerable difficulty I managed to buy a round.

Mr. Zeppelin raised an eyebrow at me. "Merv and I have been discussing a matter," he announced, "on which we would appreciate your views, gentlemen - the Canadian identity."

"The Canadian what?" asked Fred.

"Yes," said Mr. Zeppelin firmly, with a wink at me.

"Eh?" said Fred.

"To be more explicit," explained Mr. Zeppelin, "the Canadian identity. What, oh what, is a Canadian?"

"That's easy," said Fred. "A guy who lives in Canada."

"True," nodded Mr. Zeppelin. "But what we are seeking is a delineation of the characteristics which epitomize a Canadian. In a word, the apotheosis Canadensis."

"Stop your high-falutin' bull and say what you mean," suggested Speed.

"Very well," sighed Mr. Zeppelin gustily. "What is there about a Canadian that makes him different from any other nationality?"

"He lives in Canada," said Fred doggedly.

"Sure," interjected Roscoe, "but what he is getting at, in his usual fancy-pantsy way, is what's a Canadian got that makes him different from a Yank or a Limey or anybody else. Right?"

"Right," nodded Mr. Zeppelin.

"I've heard say," commented Mike, "that when the Yanks export toilet seats to Canada they cut them in half because they think we're half-assed Americans."

"To hell we are," objected Roscoe loudly. "An American is just a loud mouth attached to a pocket book."

"You're just mad because his pocket book is full and yours ain't," said Speed. "I think Americans got an inferiority complex." He looked pleased with his own sagacity.

"They sure hide it well," complained Roscoe. "What the American government ought to do is require each guy applying for a passport to take an examination in simple, garden-variety good manners. That would sure help a lot."

"Oh, go on, you guys," interposed Fred. "Americans are not all that bad. When you go to the States you couldn't ask for nicer people. They're friendly and can't do enough for you. And when they're up here they're real fine visitors. Don't let the occasional loud mouth cheese you off on the others."

"Well, gentlemen," interposed Mr. Zeppelin, "there seems to be some reservations about the Americans, but let me put it to you this way-who would you rather have instead of them for neighbours, the English, French, Russians, Chinese?" There was a pause while the group thought this over. "It gives one to ponder, doesn't it?"

Roscoe was the first to comment. "I guess if you've got to have neighbours the Americans are the best you could have."

"Yeah," agreed Speed. "They're okay really. Thank heavens they're friendly. They could take us over in twenty minutes if they wanted to. I just wish they didn't talk so bloody much. But," he wrinkled his forehead, "I guess a curtain of talk beats an iron curtain any old day." He looked surprised at his own cleverness.

"I wouldn't want the English next door," said Fred. "I don't like tea and their beer tastes like it had been passed through a horse."

"Jeeze, if we had the Russians down there we'd sure have our nuts in a nutcracker," said Speed. "Across the Arctic Circle's close enough."

"We almost had them on our doorstep, you know," I said. "The Americans bought Alaska from them."

"They did?" said Fred. "Well, that's once the Yanks spent their dough sensibly."

"I sure wouldn't want a French nation to the south of us," said Roscoe. "Think of the trouble we'd have with Quebec then."

"Yeah," said Fred, "then we'd be the minority group around here. Wow."

"If that were so," said Mr. Zeppelin, "wouldn't we be doing the same as the French Canadians are doing-trying to maintain our language, customs and identity?"

"Yeah, we sure would," agreed Roscoe. "It helps you to figure what the Frenchies are trying to do, doesn't it? Anyhow, I've always said let them do what they want in Quebec-it's their part of the country. But there's no way they're going to make me learn to speak French."

"They don't want to have to learn to speak English," said Mr. Zeppelin.

"That's their privilege."

"Then you won't be able to communicate."

"We've been getting along all right so far. I've never figured what the fuss was about, or what the French really wanted. If they'd just say it plain I'd say okay so long as it wasn't going to muck up Canada as a country."

"I don't see why the French should get special treatment. We Ukrainians don't get it," objected Mike.

"You can talk Ukrainian if you want to," said Roscoe.

"Yeah, but it ain't official."

"So what? I don't see that matters."

"You can't roll back the pages of history," said Mr. Zeppelin pontifically. "And you can't welsh on a deal. A contract's a contract."

"Well, I didn't sign it," complained Mike.

"I sure wouldn't want the Chinese down there," said Fred. "They don't believe in democracy."

"Do you?" challenged Mr. Zeppelin.

Fred looked surprised. "Of course."

"Why?"

Fred was nonplussed. Roscoe picked it up.

"For one thing, you can sit in a beer parlor and criticize the government without some gendarme coming along with a gun and sticking you in the clink."

"A good point," nodded Mr. Zeppelin. "But are you satisfied with the way democracy works in Canada?"

"Well, no," said Speed.

"The main problem," stated Mike, "is that there just don't seem to be a way you can stop them in Ottawa from raising taxes and taking more and more of your money."

"Pretty soon there won't be any problem," said Fred. "The government will take all of it and then you're working for them."

"Don't you think the government can spend your money more wisely than you can yourself?" asked Mr. Zeppelin with a wink at me. There was a general negative response to this question.

"At the last election," said Fred, "I voted Conservative because they were promising to give away more than the socialists were."

"Why do that if you don't want big brother to spend your money?" I asked.

"Because none of the parties were promising to take less and if whoever goes in is going to take all my money, I have to vote for the guys that are going to give me the most back."

"I don't quite follow that," I confessed.

"It's sort of a bird in the hand," explained Fred.

"You get a bird in the hand, you get a handful of bird shit," observed Mike.

"The big problem is that as soon as you elect those guys in Ottawa you lose control over them," said Roscoe vehemently. "The only thing to do is to return the power to the people."

"How are you going to do that?" I asked.

"Easy." Roscoe hitched his chair forward. "Have a plebiscite on every money by-law proposed. The little brothers would soon smarten up the big brothers on all their giveaways."

"Not feasible," I objected.

"Yes, it is," stated Roscoe. "By telephone and telecommunication and with the use of a computer. Every voter would have a number and by touching a 'yes' or 'no' button on his phone he could vote on every big issue."

"Not everyone has a phone," Mike pointed out.

"Most do and those that don't could register his voting number with the nearest phone. It's perfectly feasible." He launched into a long explanation of the technicalities involved. Apparently he worked for the telephone company and had a good grasp of the machinery required. I couldn't follow the explanations but his proposal did seem to have a good deal of merit if it were technically possible, which he swore it was.

Mr. Zeppelin had certainly been right about each table in the huge taproom being an island unto itself. Although there was a general hum of voices we were able to carry on our discussions without much difficulty. We had numerous interruptions due to the arrival of more beer, to visits from passing friends and to frequent trips to the bathroom.

When Roscoe had finished his dissertation and answered numerous questions and criticisms, Mr. Zeppelin cocked an eye at me, harrumphed and said, "Another point Merv and I have argued about is the importance of education. Your appraisal, gentlemen."

"Everybody should be educated," observed Fred, who apparently always said the obvious.

"Up to the extent of their ability," added Roscoe, "and not

beyond. People who get educated beyond their ability to handle it are useless and become university professors." Mr. Zeppelin smiled sweetly at me. I kept my cool.

"I wish to hell I hade more education," observed Mike. "Then I might have amounted to something. Ignorance isn't bliss, it's a pain in the ass."

"So do I," admitted Roscoe. "I had a chance to go on with my education but I was a foolish kid and didn't. I missed my opportunity and then it was too late."

"The time to shoot bears is when there's bears around," stated Mike.

"Everybody's got to have some education," said Roscoe, "but advanced education isn't magic. A smart guy can get along without it, although he'd do better with it. But you take a jerk and give him a university education, all you've got is an educated jerk. Some jerks don't come in to full bloom till they're fertilized by education. But you take a good guy and give him an education, he's still a good guy and better for it."

"Not always," objected Mike. "I've known some good kids who went to university and came out real jerks."

"Yeah, that happens," admitted Roscoe. "They may get full of themselves and look down on their folks that sweated it out for them and on the taxpayers who made it possible. And some of them come out fruity as nutcake. But the guys that are prepared to work are real fine types and an asset to the country. If they come out with limp wrists then to hell with them."

The conversation turned to city politics, generally thought to be a shambles but considered more controllable than federal affairs since the aldermen were more readily available. Various local issues were debated vigorously but inconclusively. Efforts by Mr. Zeppelin to get the men to describe the Canadian identity were unsuccessful beyond a strong affirmation that Canadians were a unique breed, different from any other. Just how they were different was not clear.

Finally Mr. Zeppelin banged his glass down loudly on the table for attention.

"And now gentlemen," he announced, "we come to the cruncher of the evening. What is truth?"

"What do you mean, what is truth?" asked a puzzled Speed.

"If I could answer your question, sir, I wouldn't have needed to ask mine," replied Mr. Zeppelin ponderously.

"I don't know what it is," said Roscoe wisely, laying a finger

140

along his nose. "But I know where it is."

"Where?" asked Mr. Zeppelin.

"In the vest pocket of the prime minister," replied Roscoe. Mr. Zeppelin laughed delightedly.

"No, it ain't," said Speed. "It's in the vest pocket of the pope."

"The pope doesn't wear a vest," objected Fred.

"In either event we're not apt to see much of it," laughed Mr. Zeppelin.

"Anyhow the answer is easy," stated Fred the literalist. "Truth is not telling lies."

I decided to take part in the conversation. "That's part of it. But surely there's more to truth than just a lack of error. Is it not an entity of itself? Is there not more to goodness than a lack of evil; is there not more to knowledge than a lack of ignorance; could not-," I became aware that Mr. Zeppelin was shaking his head unobtrusively at me. This alerted me to the fact that the beer was getting to me. I was talking like a professor. Certainly I was being philosophically naive.

"I, uh, am just asking questions. It's the beer talking," I ended up rather lamely.

Roscoe was regarding me intently with his dark intelligent eyes. "I think maybe you've got something. Truth has to be always right, unchanging. Therefore can it be a positive thing? Yes, I see. If it is true it is good, if you believe in goodness. Yeah, truth would have to be good. Very interesting." He pulled at his lower lip. Fred and Speed were looking completely baffled. Mike, however, was following him closely. Mr. Zeppelin beamed like a benign Buddha.

"Could there be a peculiarly Canadian truth?" I asked.

"Not if truth is unchangeable. But I'm sure everybody sees truth differently so there could be a Canadian slant on what truth is, which would be characteristic," said Roscoe slowly.

"What would be your own personal approach to truth?" I asked.

Roscoe cogitated over that for a few minutes. "My thoughts are tangled up like a fishing line back-lash, but I would say that truth has to be the highest good. To me that would be kindness. The sweetest goodness a guy can have in his heart is kindness."

"I'd say it a little differently," said Mike. "I'm a simple minded old bastard and kind of old-fashioned. What you guys are saying about truth makes it clear to me that truth is God. God is unchanging. God is good; God is-,"

"Truth is not telling lies," reiterated Fred doggedly.

In the process of draining my glass of beer I looked through the bottom of the glass at the room. The scene was caught and condensed in fragments of shimmering colour. As I rotated the glass, colours, lights and faces changed in kaleidoscopic variety. I studied the scene for several minutes.

"There's Canada," I said solemnly. I put down the glass to squint at Mr. Zeppelin. "You have two heads," I informed him.

"Oh, oh," said Speed.

"I'm not surprised," said Mr. Zeppelin. "Happens to me all the time when I drink too much."

A little later, Mr. Zeppelin directed my wavering steps out to the car. We sang a fine rendition of *Moonlight Bay* all the way home, my wheezy baritone rather overwhelmed by his magnificent basso profundo. When we arrived in front of my house he came around to my side of the car to help me out. We weaved our way up the sidewalk.

"Will I see you Monday, usual place, usual time?" he asked.

"No, I'm afraid not," I answered. "I'm leaving on Monday to give this paper we've been working on. I'll have to write it up on Shunday." I found I had developed an unfortunate tendency to shish my esses.

"Have you found out what the Canadian identity is then, Professor?"

"Yes, Mr. Zelepin," I said speaking very carefully. "I am happy to say our researches have not been in vain. Everything finally fell into place during the course of the evening. 'The search is the discovery', as you said. I saw it all very clearly in the bottom of a beer glass. Canadians are wonderful people and I love every one of them." I made a great hugging motion, keeling over into a bed of snapdragons.

Mr. Zeppelin picked me up and set me on my feet. "You're down the line with John Henry on wheels there, Professor."

"Toot, toot," I said, pulling an imaginary whistle cord.

"Huff, huff, huff," laughed Mr. Zeppelin, as he guided me up the steps to my door.